# Electromagnetic Fields

## R. V. Buckley

MACMILLAN

First published 1988
Reprinted 1990

Published by
MACMILLAN EDUCATION LTD
Houndmills, Basingstoke, Hampshire RG21 2XS
and London
Companies and representatives
throughout the world

Typeset by TecSet Ltd,
Wallington, Surrey
Printed in Hong Kong

British Library Cataloguing in Publication Data
Buckley, Ruth V.
Work out electromagnetic fields.—
(Macmillan work out series).
1. Electromagnetic Fields—Problems,
exercises, etc.
I. Title
530.1'41          QC665.E4
ISBN 0–333–45126–0

# Contents

# Acknowledgements

The author and publishers wish to thank the following who have kindly given permission for the use of their examination questions:

> The Institution of Electrical Engineers
> The Council of Engineering Institutions
> The Engineering Council
> Leeds Polytechnic

Over many years the questions set by the various examination boards have improved the teaching of electromagnetic theory. Everyone interested in field theory realises that the subject is very basic to the teaching of electrical engineering as well as physics and owes a debt to the boards for the challenge that new examination questions bring to engineering education.

The author wishes to thank everyone who has helped in the preparation of this book and in particular to express her appreciation of her friend Mr D. H. Trevena, for making many constructive comments and for improving the presentation of the material.

The examination boards accept no responsibility whatsoever for the accuracy or method in the answers given in this book, to actual questions set by them. The answers are the entire responsibility of the author.

# Introduction

Although most electrical and electronic engineering courses include the study of electric and magnetic field theory, it is usually recognised that on most courses much of the subject material can be and is separated out under special headings.

The 'work out' study covers the electromagnetic theory under seven major headings — electron ballistics is separated from electrostatics and electromagnetic field under steady state conditions, with a section on time-varying fields, Maxwell's equations and their relations to each media property and finally a section on waveguide developments.

The problems here have been chosen to avoid repetition as far as possible in each of the worked examples and unworked problem sections; some questions require standard proofs, while others have been included to give a general picture of the type of questions asked in examinations.

The questions vary in their level of difficulty, and the author hopes that this will enable the book to be used at several stages of a degree or diploma course.

## Examination Technique

No student can expect to pass examinations without a sound knowledge of the subject material to be examined, but he or she may improve their chances by attention to the following.

### The Candidate's Presentation

When a candidate is faced with an examination paper, he or she may avoid common errors (which can seriously prejudice the performance) and present the work most favourably by attention to the following advice.

(a) *Choice*  Take time to read through the whole paper, decide on the questions to be answered, and mark them in order of preferences; note any rubric concerning compulsory questions on restricted choice from a sectional paper.

(b) *Timing*  Do not spend too much time on a question (e.g. with five questions to answer in 3 hours, not more than 30–40 minutes should be spent on each). It is unwise to persist with complicated and laborious work that seems to be leading nowhere: the answer sought by the examiners is unlikely to involve several pages of analysis.

(c) *Interpretation*  Carefully read each question before starting to answer it: answer the question set, not some alternative of your own; do not just 'describe' when the question states, compare; do not omit an essential part of the question.

(d) *Presentation*  Either read each answer carefully after writing it or allow adequate time towards the end of the examination period, to revise and correct the work.

(e) *Formulae*  Do not attempt to memorise extensive lists of formulae. A candidate is expected to know (by common usage and familiarity rather than by a conscious effort of memory) a few simple expressions directly based on fundamental laws and principles. Complex formulae will normally be quoted in the question, or the candidate will be asked to develop them from 'first principles'.

### The Examiner's Requirements

In assessing a candidate's ability, the examiner looks particularly for:

(a) Sound knowledge of the appropriate fundamental principles; facility in the analysis of problems based thereon; and a clear and explicit understanding of the methods used and approximations legitimately made.

(b) Facility in numerical and graphical work in the solution of (in the examination sense) 'practical' engineering problems; logical layout of steps in the working; and an appreciation of practical orders of size and of numerical accuracy.

(c) Collective marshalling of logic and critical arguments for and against the choice of methods, equipment and lines of action.

(d) Some knowledge, derived from wider reading and professional motivation, of the general trend of modern developments.

(e) Ability to present descriptive answers legibly, concisely and grammatically; the use, where appropriate, of clear and neat freehand sketches.

# Standard Data

Magnetic space constant: $\mu_0 = 4\pi \times 10^{-7}$ H/m

Electric space constant: $\epsilon_0 = \dfrac{1}{36\pi \times 10^9}$ F/m

Electron charge/rest mass ratio: $\dfrac{e}{m} = 1.76 \times 10^{11}$ C/kg

Velocity of electromagnetic radiation in free space: $= 3 \times 10^8$ m/s

# 1 Electron Ballistics

## 1.1 Fact Sheet

A *scalar* is a physical quantity which is completely defined by its magnitude. Examples include mass, length, time, current, voltage and temperature.

A *vector* is a physical quantity which is not completely defined unless its direction as well as its magnitude is specified. Examples include velocity, acceleration, force, electric field strength, current density and magnetic field intensity.

For the dynamics of particle motion, the electron is visualised as a particle with negative electric charge $-e$ ($1.602 \times 10^{-19}$ C). It is associated with a mass $m$ which increases as the velocity of the electron increases towards that of the velocity of light, $c$ ($3 \times 10^8$ m/s).

From the theory of relativity

$$m = \frac{9.11 \times 10^{-31}}{\left[1 - \dfrac{v^2}{c^2}\right]^{\frac{1}{2}}} \text{ kg}$$

where $m$ is the particle mass at a velocity $v$, and $c$ is the velocity of light.

However, it is usual to assume that the mass is constant, $9.11 \times 10^{-31}$ kg, for all velocities up to values approximately one-third of the velocity of light.

### (a) Particle Acceleration

If the particles are free to move in an electric field, Newton's laws of motion may be used to determine the resultant path and position of the particle. Assume that an electron is placed in an electrostatic field of strength $\overline{E}$ V/m. Then the force exerted on it is

$$\overline{F} = -e\overline{E} \text{ N}$$

while the force required to produce an acceleration $\overline{f}$ is given by

$$\overline{F} = m\overline{f} \text{ N}$$

Hence,

$$\overline{f} = -\frac{e}{m}\,\overline{E} \text{ m/s}^2$$

If the potential under consideration is $V$ volts, then, from electrostatic theory,

$$\overline{E} = \frac{\partial V}{\partial x} \text{ V/m}$$

where $x$ is the displacement of the electron from some reference point in the field.

Therefore,

$$\overline{f} = \frac{e}{m}\,\frac{\partial V}{\partial x} \text{ m/s}^2$$

### (b) Energy Relationship

If an electron starts with zero velocity in an electrostatic field, then its velocity at a point where the potential is $V$ volts is given by

$$\overline{v} = \left[ 2 \, \frac{e}{m} V \right]^{\frac{1}{2}} \text{ m/s}$$

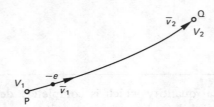

**Fig. 1.1**

From Figure 1.1 an electron moving from point P to point Q, via any path, yields

$$\text{gain in kinetic energy} = \text{loss in potential energy}$$

Therefore,

$$\overline{v}_2^2 - \overline{v}_1^2 = \frac{2e}{m} \, (V_2 - V_1)$$

Note that so far the equations do not involve any coordinate system, except the arbitrary distance $x$.

### (c) Uniform Electrostatic Field

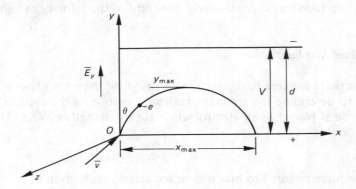

**Fig. 1.2**

Consider an electron entering the field at point $O$ in Figure 1.2 with a velocity $v$, making an angle $\theta$ with the vertical. It is necessary to use a coordinate system to indicate which planes the electron will move through:

$$\overline{E}_x = \overline{E}_z = 0; \quad \overline{E}_y = - \frac{V}{d} \text{ V/m}$$

Consider a point in the field with coordinates $x, y$. The vertical and horizontal components of velocity are $v \cos \theta$ and $v \sin \theta$, so that, from Newton's laws of motion,

$$x = \overline{v} \sin \theta \, t$$

$$y = \overline{v} \cos \theta \, t + \tfrac{1}{2} \overline{f}_y t^2$$

Now

$$\overline{f}_y = - \frac{e}{m} \overline{E}_y$$

Eliminate $t$ between the equations for $x$ and $y$; hence,

$$y = \frac{x}{\tan \theta} - \frac{1}{2} \times \frac{e}{m} \times \overline{E}_y \times \frac{x^2}{v^2 \sin^2 \theta}$$

This is the equation of a parabola.

### (d) Uniform Magnetic Field

A charged particle moving in a magnetic field experiences a force only if it moves at an angle to the field and the force is perpendicular to both the direction of motion and the direction of the applied field, as shown in Figure 1.3.

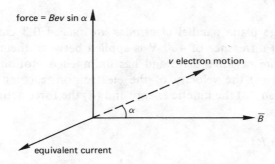

**Fig. 1.3**

Consider an electron injected into a magnetic field with velocity $v$ m/s, as shown in Figure 1.4. The field, of strength $\overline{B}$ T, is into the plane of the paper.

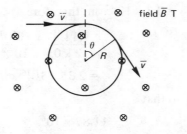

**Fig.1.4**

Now the magnetic force due to the field, the charge on the electron and its velocity is given by

$$\overline{F} = \overline{B}e\overline{v} \quad \text{N}$$

It will be held on a circular path of radius $R$ by a centrifugal force equal to $\frac{mv^2}{R}$ ;

therefore,

$$\overline{B} e \overline{v} = \frac{m \overline{v}^2}{R} \text{ when } \alpha = 90°$$

$$R = \frac{m \overline{v}}{e \overline{B}}$$

$$\text{period of rotation } T = \frac{2\pi R}{\overline{v}} = \frac{2\pi m}{e \overline{B}} \text{ s}$$

Note that the period depends on the field strength only.

## 1.2  Worked Examples

### Example 1.1

Two large plane parallel electrodes are placed 0.3 cm apart in a vacuum and a potential difference of 400 V is applied between them. If an electron starts from rest at the negative plate and has unimpeded motion to the positive electrode, calculate (a) the velocity of the electron on reaching the positive plate, (b) the time taken, (c) the kinetic energy and (d) the force acting on it.

### Solution 1.1

(a) $\overline{v} = [2 \times 1.76 \times 10^{11} \times 400]^{\frac{1}{2}}$ m/s

$\underline{= 11.87 \times 10^6 \text{ m/s}}$

Note change/mass ratio $e/m = 1.76 \times 10^{11}$ C/kg.

(b) Using Newton's law of motion to obtain the acceleration during the electron's period of travel,

$$v^2 = u^2 + 2fs$$

Now $u = 0$ and $s = 0.3 \times 10^{-2}$ m; therefore

$$f = \frac{(11.87 \times 10^6)^2}{2 \times 0.3 \times 10^{-2}} \text{ m/s}^2$$

$$= 2.35 \times 10^{16} \text{ m/s}^2$$

Also $v = u + ft$, so that

$$t = \frac{11.87 \times 10^6}{2.35 \times 10^{16}} = \underline{5.05 \times 10^{-10} \text{ s}}$$

(c) Kinetic energy $= \frac{1}{2} mv^2$ J

$$= \frac{1}{2} \times 9.1 \times 10^{-31} \times (11.87 \times 10^6)^2 \text{ J}$$

$$= \underline{6.41 \times 10^{-17} \text{ J}}$$

(d) Force acting on the electron $= mf$  N

$$= 9.1 \times 10^{-31} \times 2.35 \times 10^{16} \text{ N}$$

$$= \underline{2.14 \times 10^{-14} \text{ N}}$$

**Example 1.2**

An electron is projected with an initial energy of 600 eV in a horizontal direction into an electrostatic field of strength $10^5$ V/m which acts vertically upwards. Deduce the equations giving the trajectory of the electron and calculate its position after $10^{-9}$ s.

(Leeds Polytechnic)

*Solution 1.2*

The path of the electron is shown in the diagram.

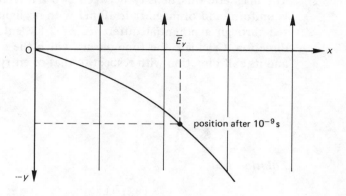

The electron-volt (eV) is the energy acquired by an electron when it is projected through a potential difference of 1 V. Therefore,

$$\text{initial energy of the electron} = 600 \times 1.6 \times 10^{-19} \text{ J}$$

$$= 9.6 \times 10^{-17} \text{ J}$$

$$\text{initial velocity } \bar{v}_0 = \left[ \frac{2 \times 9.6 \times 10^{-17}}{9.1 \times 10^{-31}} \right]^{\frac{1}{2}} \text{ m/s}$$

$$= 14.53 \times 10^6 \text{ m/s}$$

This velocity $\bar{v}_0$ is directed along the 0–$x$ axis, and the position after $t$ s is

$$x = v_0 t$$

$$= 14.53 \times 10^6 \times 10^{-9} \text{ m}$$

$$= \underline{0.014\,53 \text{ m}}$$

Since the field direction is upwards, the force on the electron is downwards and the trajectory will be as shown in the diagram:

$$\text{force} = -e\bar{E} \text{ N}$$

$$\text{acceleration} = -\frac{e}{m} \bar{E} \text{ m/s}^2$$

Using Newton's second law of motion, the position $y$ after $t$ s is given by

$$y = \tfrac{1}{2} ft^2 = -\tfrac{1}{2} \frac{e\bar{E}}{m} t^2 \text{ m}$$

and, if a substitution is made for $t$, then

$$y = -\frac{e\bar{E}}{2m} \frac{x^2}{v_0^2} \text{ m}$$

5

which is the equation of a parabola. After $10^{-9}$ s

$$y = -\tfrac{1}{2} \times 1.76 \times 10^{-11} \times 10^5 \times 10^{-18} \text{ m}$$

$$= -0.0088 \text{ m}$$

## Example 1.3

The magnetic flux density between two flat circular pole faces of diameter 0.1 m is uniform and of magnitude 10 mT with negligible fringing. An electron accelerated through a potential difference of 2 kV enters the magnetic field in a radial direction. Calculate the time during which the electron is between the pole faces and its exit direction with respect to that of entry.

(IEE Part 3)

### Solution 1.3

The initial velocity $\bar{u} = \left[ \dfrac{2eV}{m} \right]^{\frac{1}{2}}$

$$= [2 \times 1.76 \times 10^{11} \times 2000]^{\frac{1}{2}} \text{ m/s}$$

$$= 2.65 \times 10^7 \text{ m/s}$$

The path radius $r$ is given by

$$r = \frac{mu}{eB}$$

$$= \frac{2.65 \times 10^7}{1.76 \times 10^{11} \times 10 \times 10^{-3}} \text{ m}$$

$$= 0.015 \text{ m}$$

The electron enters the field, follows a circular path and emerges radially. From the geometry, the exit direction makes the angle given by

$$2 \times \tan^{-1} \frac{0.015}{0.05} = 33.4°$$

to the entry direction. (*Hint:* Sketch the circular path in relation to the circular pole face.)

$$\text{Path length} = \frac{146.6}{360} \times 2 \times \pi \times 0.015 \text{ m}$$

$$= 0.038 \text{ m}$$

$$\text{Period of rotation} = \frac{2\pi m}{eB} = 3.57 \times 10^{-9} \text{ s}$$

$$\text{Time for the electron to travel the path length} = \frac{0.038}{2 \times \pi \times 0.015} \times 3.57 \times 10^{-9} \text{ s}$$

$$= 1.45 \text{ ns}$$

**Example 1.4**

A stream of electrons, passing through a hole in a large metal plate A, makes an angle of 60° with the plane of A. Parallel to and 50 mm above A there is a second plate B, maintained at a potential lower than that of A. Obtain an expression for the trajectory of the electron stream between the plates.

If the velocity on passing through the plate A is $20 \times 10^6$ m/s, at what potential will the electron stream just graze plate B?

(CEI Part 2)

*Solution 1.4*

The electron stream enters the field at O with a velocity $u$ making 60° with the plane of plate A — see diagram; at some point on the trajectory the coordinates are $x$ and $y$:

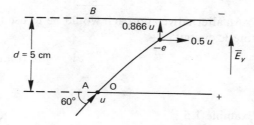

$$x = 0.5\,ut$$

$$y = 0.866\,ut + \tfrac{1}{2}\,\bar{f}_y\,t^2$$

where

$$\bar{f}_y = -\frac{e}{m}\,\bar{E}_y$$

and

$$\bar{E}_y = -\frac{V}{d}$$

Eliminating $t$ yields

$$y = 1.732\,x - \tfrac{1}{2} \times 1.76 \times 10^{11}\,\bar{E}_y \times \frac{x^2}{0.25\,u^2}$$

$$y = 1.732\,x - 3.52 \times 10^{11}\,\bar{E}_y\,\frac{x^2}{u^2}$$

For the stream to just graze the upper plate with an entry velocity of $20 \times 10^6$ m/s, one needs to find $dy/dt$ and equate the result to zero, thus giving the time to reach a maximum vertical displacement:

$$\frac{dy}{dt} = 0.866\,\bar{u} - \frac{e}{m}\,\bar{E}_y\,t = 0$$

$$t = \frac{0.866 \times \bar{u}}{1.76 \times 10^{11} \times \bar{E}_y}$$

7

Therefore $y_{max} = 0.05 = 0.866 \, u \times t - \frac{1}{2} \times \frac{e}{m} \times \overline{E}_y \times t^2$

$$0.05 = \frac{(0.866 \, u)^2}{1.76 \times 10^{11} \times \overline{E}_y} - \frac{1}{2} \frac{(0.866 \, u)^2}{1.76 \times 10^{11} \times \overline{E}_y}$$

$$0.05 = \frac{1}{2} \times \frac{(0.866 \, u)^2}{1.76 \times 10^{11} \times \overline{E}_y}$$

$$\overline{E}_y = \frac{1}{2} \times \frac{0.866^2 \times (20 \times 10^6)^2}{1.76 \times 10^{11} \times 0.05} \text{ V/m}$$

$$= 17\,044 \text{ V/m}$$

Now

$$\overline{E}_y = \frac{V}{d}$$

Therefore

$$V = 17\,044 \times 0.05 \text{ V}$$

$$= \underline{852 \text{ V}}$$

An alternative approach would be to use the relationship between potential and kinetic energy:

$$eV = \frac{1}{2} m \, (0.866 \, \overline{u})^2 \text{ J}$$

## Example 1.5

A pair of concentric, cylindrical electrodes are in a vacuum. The outer electrode at zero potential has an inside radius $R$. The outside radius of the inner electrode is $r$ and the positive potential of this electrode is $V_0$. Derive an expression for the potential at any radius $x$ between the electrodes, remote from the ends of the cylinders.

An electron is injected radially outwards through a small hole in the inner electrode with a velocity $u_0 = 5.2 \times 10^6$ m/s. If $R = 24$ mm, $r = 8$ mm and $V = 50$ V, calculate the velocity of the electron where $x = 20$ mm, and also the velocity of the electron on impact with the outer electrode. A profile of the concentric electrodes is shown in the diagram.

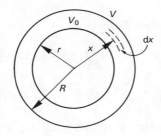

(IEE Part 3)

*Solution 1.5*

The potential $V$ at any radius $x$ is obtained from

$$V = -\int \overline{E} \, dx$$

That is,

$$V = -\int_R^x \frac{q\,\mathrm{d}x}{2\pi x\,\epsilon_0}$$

where $q$ C is the charge per unit length of electrode into the plane of the paper. Therefore,

$$V_x = \frac{q}{2\pi\epsilon_0} \log_e \frac{R}{x}$$

When $x = r$, $V_x = V_0$; therefore,

$$V_x = \frac{V_0}{\log_e\left(\dfrac{R}{r}\right)} \log_e \frac{R}{x}$$

When $x = 20$ mm,

$$V_x = \frac{50}{\log_e\left(\dfrac{2.4}{0.8}\right)} \log_e \frac{2.4}{2} = \underline{8.3 \text{ V}}$$

From an energy basis, as the electron decelerates,

$$\text{gain in potential energy} = \text{loss in kinetic energy}$$
$$e \times (50 - 8.3) = \tfrac{1}{2} \times m \times [(5.2 \times 10^6)^2 - \overline{v}_x^2]$$
$$\overline{v}_x^2 = 27.04 \times 10^{12} - 14.68 \times 10^{12}$$
$$= 12.36 \times 10^{12}$$
$$\overline{v}_x = 3.52 \times 10^6 \text{ m/s}$$

On impact where the potential is zero

$$\overline{v}_x^2 = 27.04 \times 10^{12} - 17.6 \times 10^{12}$$
$$= 9.44 \times 10^{12}$$
$$\underline{\overline{v}_x = 3.07 \times 10^6 \text{ m/s}}$$

## Example 1.6

The potential difference between two parallel plates A and B in a vacuum is $V = V_0 + V_m \cos \omega t$, with plate A maintained at zero potential.

The distance between the plates is $d$. At time $t = 0$ an electron at rest is released from plate A and attracted towards plate B. Derive expressions for the subsequent velocity and position of the electron in relation to $\omega t$.

If $V_0 = 3$ V, $V_m = 15$ V, $\omega = 5 \times 10^7$ rad/s and $d = 80$ mm, calculate the kinetic energy of the electron and its distance from plate A (a) when $\omega t = \pi$ and (b) when $\omega t = 2\pi$.

(Leeds Polytechnic)

## Solution 1.6

Remember that this is an a.c. field problem which affects the calculation of the expression for the electric intensity,

$$\overline{E}_y = -\frac{\mathrm{d}V}{\mathrm{d}y} = \frac{-V_0 - V_m \cos \omega t}{d}$$

The acceleration is given by

$$\bar{f}_y = -\frac{e}{m} \times \bar{E}_y = \frac{e}{m}\left[V_0 + \frac{V_m \cos \omega t}{d}\right]$$

The vertical velocity is given by

$$\bar{v}_y = \int_0^t f_y \, dt + u = \frac{e}{md}\left[V_0 t + \frac{V_m}{\omega} \sin \omega t\right] + u$$

But $u = 0$ — no initial velocity. Therefore,

$$\bar{v}_y = \frac{e}{md}\left[V_0 t + \frac{V_m}{\omega} \sin \omega t\right]$$

The vertical displacement is given by

$$y = \int_0^t v_y \, dt = \frac{e}{md}\left[\frac{V_0 t^2}{2} - \frac{V_m}{\omega^2} \cos \omega t\right] + k'$$

When $t = 0$, $y = 0$; therefore,

$$k' = \frac{eV_m}{m \times d \times \omega^2}$$

therefore,

$$y = \frac{e}{md}\left[V_0 \frac{t^2}{2} - \frac{V_m}{\omega^2} \cos \omega t + \frac{V_m}{\omega^2}\right]$$

When $V_0 = 3$, $V_m = 15$, $\omega = 5 \times 10^7$ and $d = 0.08$ m,

$$\bar{v}_y = \frac{1.76 \times 10^{11}}{0.08}\left[3t + \frac{15}{5 \times 10^7} \sin 5 \times 10^7 \, t\right]$$

$$= 2.2 \times 10^{12} \, [3t + 0.3 \times 10^{-6} \sin 5 \times 10^7 \, t]$$

When $\omega t = \pi$,

$$\bar{v}_y = 2.2 \times 10^{12}\left[\frac{3 \times \pi}{5 \times 10^7} + 0\right] = 0.415 \times 10^6 \text{ m/s}$$

and

$$\text{kinetic energy} = \tfrac{1}{2} \times 9.11 \times 10^{-31} \times 0.172 \times 10^{12} \text{ J}$$

$$= 0.783 \times 10^{-19} \text{ J}$$

Also

$$y = 2.2 \times 10^{12}\left[\frac{3}{2} t^2 - \frac{15}{25 \times 10^{14}} \cos \omega t + \frac{15}{25 \times 10^{14}}\right]$$

$$= 2.2 \times 10^{12}\left[1.5 \times \frac{\pi^2}{25 \times 10^{14}} + \frac{0.6}{10^{14}} + \frac{0.6}{10^{14}}\right] \text{ m}$$

$$= 0.02 \times 1.792 \text{ m}$$

$$= \underline{39.4 \text{ mm}}$$

When $\omega t = 2\pi$,

$$\bar{v}_y = 2.2 \times 10^{12}\left[\frac{3 \times 2\pi}{5 \times 10^7}\right] = 8.3 \times 10^5 \text{ m/s}$$

and

$$\text{kinetic energy} = \tfrac{1}{2} \times 9.11 \times 10^{-31} \times 68.89 \times 10^{10} \text{ J}$$

$$= \underline{314 \times 10^{-21} \text{ J}}$$

Also

$$y = 2.2 \times 10^{12} \left[ \frac{3}{2} \times \frac{4\pi^2}{25 \times 10^{14}} - \frac{0.6}{10^{14}} + \frac{0.6}{10^{14}} \right] \text{ m}$$

$$= \underline{52.1 \text{ mm}}$$

### Example 1.7

The spacing between the parallel plates of a capacitor in a vacuum is 10 mm. There is a steady potential difference of 1.76 kV between the plates and a uniform magnetic field of 0.01 T directed parallel to the plates when an electron is released from the negative plate with zero velocity. This is shown in the diagram.

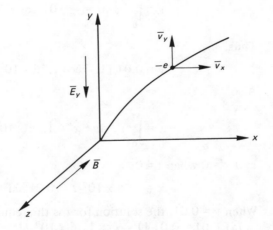

Calculate (a) the transit time of the electron, (b) the velocity with which the electron strikes the positive plate, (c) the angle of incidence on impact.

(Leeds Polytechnic)

### Solution 1.7

Using basic force relations,

$$m \frac{d\bar{v}_x}{dt} = Be\,\bar{v}_y$$

$$m \frac{d\bar{v}_y}{dt} = e\,\bar{E}_y - Be\,\bar{v}_x$$

Now

$$\bar{E}_y = \frac{1.76 \times 10^3}{1 \times 10^{-2}} = 1.76 \times 10^5 \text{ V/m}$$

Therefore,

$$\frac{d\bar{v}_x}{dt} = 1.76 \times 10^{11} \times 0.01 \times \bar{v}_y = 1.76 \times 10^9 \times \bar{v}_y$$

$$\frac{d\bar{v}_y}{dt} = 1.76 \times 10^{11} \times 1.76 \times 10^5 - 0.01 \times 1.76 \times 10^{11} \times \bar{v}_x$$

$$= 3.1 \times 10^{16} - 1.76 \times 10^9 \times \bar{v}_x$$

$$\frac{d^2\bar{v}_y}{dt^2} = -1.76 \times 10^9 \times \frac{d\bar{v}_x}{dt}$$

Substitute for $d\bar{v}_x/dt$ to give

$$\frac{d^2\bar{v}_y}{dt^2} + 3.1 \times 10^{18} \, \bar{v}_y = 0$$

The solution of this equation is found to be $\bar{v}_y = 1.76 \times 10^7 \sin 1.76 \times 10^9 \, t$, since $\bar{v} = 0$ at $t = 0$. Thus,

$$\bar{v}_x = 1.76 \times 10^7 \, [1 - \cos 1.76 \times 10^9 \, t]$$

$$y = \int_0^t \bar{v}_y \, dt = -0.01 \cos 1.76 \times 10^9 \, t + 0.01 \cos 0$$

Thus,

$$y = 0.01 \, [1 - \cos 1.76 \times 10^9 \, t]$$

Also

$$x = \int_0^t \bar{v}_x \, dt + x' = 1.76 \times 10^7 \left[ t - \frac{\sin 1.76 \times 10^9 \, t}{1.76 \times 10^9} \right] + x'$$

and $x' = 0$ when $t = 0$:

$$x = 1.76 \times 10^7 \, t - 0.01 \sin 1.76 \times 10^9 \, t$$

When $y = 0.01$, the solution for $t$ is the required transit time.

(a) $0.01 = 0.01 \, [1 - \cos 1.76 \times 10^9 \, t]$

or

$$1.76 \times 10^9 \, t = \frac{\pi}{2}$$

$$t = \frac{\pi}{2 \times 1.76 \times 10^9} = \underline{0.89 \text{ ns}}$$

(b) To obtain the strike velocity, it is necessary to find $\bar{v}_x$ and $\bar{v}_y$ at the transit time:

$$\bar{v}_x = 1.76 \times 10^7 \sin\left[ \frac{1.76 \times 10^9 \times \pi}{1.76 \times 10^9 \times 2} \right] = 1.76 \times 10^7$$

$$\bar{v}_y = 1.76 \times 10^7 \left[ 1 - \cos \frac{\pi}{2} \right] = 1.76 \times 10^7$$

Thus,

$$\text{strike velocity} = [(1.76 \times 10^7)^2 + (1.76 \times 10^7)^2]^{\frac{1}{2}} \text{ m/s}$$

$$= \underline{2.49 \times 10^7 \text{ m/s}}$$

This checks out, using the energy relationship.

(c) The angle of incidence on impact is

$$\tan^{-1} \frac{\bar{v}_y}{\bar{v}_x}$$

$$= \tan^{-1} 1$$

$$= \underline{45°}$$

**Example 1.8**

In the diagram, a constant magnetic flux density $\bar{B}$ = 1.42 mT and a constant electric field of intensity $\bar{E}$ = 10 kV/m act in an evacuated space in a direction parallel to the $O$–$Z$ axis. At time $t$ = 0, an electron passes the origin $O$ with a velocity $u = 5 \times 10^6$ m/s in the direction $OY$, as shown in the diagram. At time

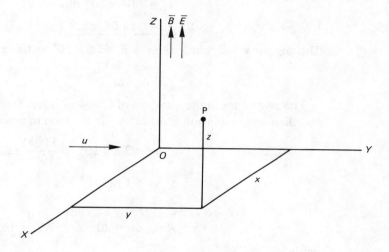

$t$ = 0.004 $\mu$s, the electron has reached the point P. Calculate the coordinates of the point P and the velocity of the electron at this point. Determine also the subsequent maximum and minimum values of the coordinates $x$ and $y$. Ignore relativistic effects.

(IEE Part 3)

*Solution 1.8*

$$\text{Initial velocity } u = \bar{v}_{0y} = 5 \times 10^6 \text{ m/s}$$

$$\bar{v}_{0x} = \bar{v}_{0z}$$

$$= 0$$

Due to the electrostatic field there is acceleration in the $-z$-direction

$$\bar{f}_z = 1.76 \times 10^{11} \times 10^4 \text{ ms}^{-2}$$

while due to the magnetic field there will be circular motion effect, and this yields

$$Be\,\bar{v}_{0y} = \frac{m\,\bar{v}_{0y}^2}{R}$$

or

$$R = \frac{m\,\bar{v}_{0y}}{eB}$$

13

Thus,

$$R = \frac{5 \times 10^6}{1.76 \times 10^{11} \times 1.42 \times 10^{-3}} \text{ m}$$

$$= 20 \text{ mm}$$

To determine the projection details of the path in the $xy$-plane, use Newton's laws of motion: $v = u + ft$ and $s = ut + \frac{1}{2}ft^2$. Hence,

$$\bar{v}_z = 0 + 1.76 \times 10^{15} \, t$$

$$z = 0 - \frac{1}{2} \times 1.76 \times 10^{15} \, t^2$$

when

$$t = 0.004 \times 10^{-6}$$

$$\bar{v}_z = 7.04 \times 10^6 \text{ m/s}$$

$$\underline{z = -14.08 \text{ mm}}$$

The angular velocity $\omega = (e/m) \times B = 2.5 \times 10^8$ rad/s and gives a period of

$$T = \frac{2\pi}{\omega} = 2.52 \times 10^{-8} \text{ s}$$

The given time in the question of 0.004 $\mu$s is less than the period time $T$, so that less than one revolution is made by the electron in reaching point P. Now

$$\omega t = 2.5 \times 10^8 \times \frac{0.004}{10^6} \text{ rad}$$

$$= 1 \text{ rad } (57.3°)$$

Thus,

$$y = R \sin \omega t = 20 \times \sin 57.3° = \underline{16.9 \text{ mm}}$$

while

$$x = R[1 - \cos \omega t] = 20 [1 - \cos 57.3°] = \underline{9.2 \text{ mm}}$$

The velocity at the point P is found by using the $Y$ and $Z$ velocity component values, i.e.

$$10^6 \times [7.04^2 + 5^2]^{\frac{1}{2}} = \underline{8.63 \times 10^6 \text{ m/s}}$$

Thus, the maximum and minimum coordinate values can be deduced as

$$\underline{Y_{max} = \pm 20 \text{ mm}}$$

$$\underline{X_{max} = + 40 \text{ mm, or } 0}$$

## Example 1.9

(a) A particle with a charge $q$ moves with a velocity $\bar{v}$ in a region occupied by an electric field with intensity $\bar{E}$ and a magnetic field with a flux density $\bar{B}$. Justify the statement that the force experienced by the particle is given by the expression $\bar{F} = q[\bar{E} + \bar{v} \times \bar{B}]$.

(b) If the electric field is zero and the magnetic field is uniform, show that the particle moves on a helical path, with a constant angular velocity perpendicular to the field and a constant linear velocity parallel to the field.

(CEI Part 2)

*Solution 1.9*

(a) By Coulomb's law, the force between two particles $q$ and $+1$ from part (a) of the diagram is given by

$$\overline{F}_s = \frac{q \times 1}{4\pi d^2 \epsilon} \ \text{N}$$

where $\epsilon$ is the permittivity of the medium. The electrical intensity $\overline{E}$ experienced by the unit positive charge $+1$ is

$$\overline{E} = \frac{q}{4\pi d^2 \epsilon} \ \text{V/m}$$

and is a vector quantity, so that the force experienced by the particle $q$ is

$$\overline{F}_s = q\overline{E} \ \text{N}$$

acting in the same direction as the vector $\overline{E}$.

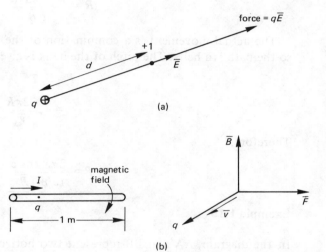

The magnetic force acts perpendicular to both the field and the velocity of the particle, as shown in part (b) of the diagram:

$$\overline{F}_m = I \times \overline{\delta l} \times \overline{B} \ \text{N}$$

In time $t$ the particle $q$ travels a distance $\overline{\delta l} = \overline{v}\delta t$ and the current is $q/\delta t$, so that $I\delta l = q\overline{v}$. Therefore,

$$\overline{F}_m = q\overline{v} \times \overline{B} \ \text{N}$$

Thus,

$$\text{total force} = q\overline{E} + q\overline{v} \times \overline{B} = \underline{q \ [\overline{E} + \overline{v} \times \overline{B} \ ]}$$

(b) If an electron enters a magnetic field at some angle $\alpha$, the force experienced by the electrons will be due to the normal component of velocity, and the motion along the line of action of the magnetic field will be unaffected.

The axial component of velocity $\overline{v}_x = \overline{v} \cos \alpha$ and the electrons will move at this rate from left to right.

The normal component of velocity is $\overline{v}_y = \overline{v} \sin \alpha$, so that the force acting on the electron, at right angles to both the field $\overline{B}$ and the velocity $\overline{v}_y$, is

$$\overline{F} = \overline{B} \ e \ \overline{v} \sin \alpha$$

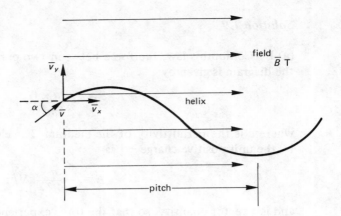

If the electron moved under this force *only*, its orbit would be circular and the radius would be

$$R = \frac{m\,\bar{v}\,\sin\alpha}{e\,\bar{B}}$$

The actual movement is a combination of the circular and the axial velocities, so the path is a helix. The pitch of the helix is given by

$$P = \bar{v}_x T$$

$$= \bar{v}_x\,\frac{2\pi R}{\bar{v}_y}$$

Therefore,

$$P = \frac{2\pi\bar{v}\,\cos\alpha}{(e/m)\,\bar{B}}$$

**Example 1.10**

In the diagram, AA and BB represent two horizontal, parallel plates distance $2y$ apart in a vacuum. A potential difference $V_2$ exists between the plates, with the

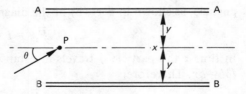

lower plate positive. An electron, accelerated through a potential difference $V_1$, enters the space between the plates centrally at P in a direction at an angle $\theta$ to the horizontal, as shown. Derive an equation for the subsequent path of the electron. Field fringing at the edges of the plate may be neglected.

*Solution 1.10*

If $\theta = 45°$, $V_2 = 200$ V and $y = 20$ mm, calculate the value of $V_1$ that will cause the electron just to graze the upper electrode and the total time then taken for the electron to reach the lower plate. The entry velocity at point P can be found from energy considerations:

$$\bar{v} = 2\left[\frac{e}{m}V_1\right]^{\frac{1}{2}} \text{ m/s}$$

$$= [2 \times 1.76 \times 10^{11} \times V_1]^{\frac{1}{2}} \text{ m/s}$$

$$= [3.52 \times 10^{11} \times V_1]^{\frac{1}{2}} \text{ m/s}$$

while

$$\text{electric field intensity, } \bar{E}_y = -\left[\frac{-V_2}{2y}\right] = \frac{V_2}{2y}$$

$$\text{force acting on the electron, } \bar{F} = -e\bar{E}_y = \frac{-eV_2}{2y}$$

The acceleration in the vertical direction $\bar{f}_y$ is found from

$$\bar{f}_y = \frac{\bar{F}_s}{m} = -\frac{eV_2}{m2y}$$

The vertical displacement is given by

$$Y = \bar{v}\sin\theta t - \frac{e}{2m}\frac{V_2}{2y}t^2$$

$(s = ut + \frac{1}{2}ft^2)$,

while the horizontal displacement is found from

$$X = v\cos\theta t$$

Now eliminate $t$ between the equations for $X$ and $Y$:

$$Y = \frac{\bar{v}\sin\theta X}{\bar{v}\cos\theta} - \frac{eV_2}{4my}\frac{X^2}{\bar{v}^2\cos^2\theta}$$

$$= X\tan\theta - \frac{eV_2}{4my}\frac{X^2}{\bar{v}^2\cos^2\theta}$$

This should be recognised as the equation to a parabola ($ax + bx^2$). For maximum height, find $dy/dt$, equate the result to zero, and so find the corresponding time:

$$\frac{dy}{dt} = \bar{v}\sin\theta - \frac{e}{m}\frac{V_2 t}{2y}$$

$$= 0$$

Thus,

$$t = \frac{\bar{v}\sin\theta\, m\, 2y}{eV_2}$$

and

$$Y_{max} = \frac{\bar{v}^2\sin^2\theta\, my}{eV_2}$$

Therefore,

$$2 \times 10^{-2} = \frac{\bar{v}^2\sin^2 45° \times 2 \times 10^{-2}}{1.76 \times 10^{11} \times 200}$$

Therefore,

$$\bar{v}^2 = 70.4 \times 10^{12}$$

$$\bar{v} = 8.39 \times 10^6 \text{ m/s}$$

Therefore,

$$V_1 = \frac{\bar{v}^2}{3.52 \times 10^{11}} \text{ V}$$

$$= \frac{70.4 \times 10^{12}}{3.52 \times 10^{11}} \text{ V}$$

$$= \underline{200 \text{ V}}$$

To find the time to travel to the lower plate, $y = -4 \times 10^{-2}$ m, measured from the *upper* plate position (remember that the electron has grazed the plate AA):

$$-4 \times 10^{-2} = -\tfrac{1}{2} \times 1.76 \times 10^{11} \times \frac{200}{2 \times 2 \times 10^{-2}} t^2$$

Therefore,

$$t^2 = \frac{16}{17.6 \times 10^{16}} \text{ s}^2$$

or

$$t = \underline{0.952 \times 10^{-8} \text{ s}}$$

The time to reach the upper plate, i.e. $Y_{max}$, is given by

$$t = \frac{8.39 \times 10^6 \times 0.707 \times 2 \times 20 \times 10^{-3}}{1.76 \times 10^{11} \times 200} \text{ s}$$

$$= 0.675 \times 10^{-8} \text{ s}$$

Total time from the starting point P $= \underline{1.63 \times 10^{-8} \text{ s}}$.

## 1.3  Unworked Problems

### Problem 1.1

A high-vacuum diode has concentric cylindrical electrodes with a potential difference $V_0$ between them. The inner electrode, of radius $r$, is at zero potential and is the cathode. The radius of the anode is $R$. Derive an expression for the potential $V$ at any radius $x$ between the electrodes.

An electron leaves the cathode in a radial direction towards the anode with an initial velocity $u_1 = 6 \times 10^6$ m/s. If $r = 5$ mm, $R = 20$ mm and $V_0 = 120$ V, calculate the velocity of the electron at radius $x = 15$ mm and the velocity of the electron on impact. Sketch the relationship between velocity and radius and estimate the transit time of the electron between cathode and anode.

(IEE Part 3)

$[8.34 \times 10^6$ m/s; $8.85 \times 10^6$ m/s; $2 \times 10^{-9}$ s]

### Problem 1.2

Electrons are accelerated through a potential difference $V_0$ to a velocity $v$. They then form two long thin and parallel pencil beams at a distance $x$ apart. A current $I$ is carried by each beam. Derive an expression for the total force per unit length between the beams. If the accelerating voltage $V_0 = 20$ kV, $x = 10$ mm and $I = 20$ mA, calculate the force acting on each beam per metre length and indicate the direction of the force.

$[0.094$ $\mu$N per metre length]

**Problem 1.3**

A cathode-ray oscilloscope has a final anode voltage of + 2 kV with respect to the cathode. Calculate the beam velocity. Parallel deflecting plates are provided, 15 mm long and 5 mm apart, their centre being 500 mm from the screen. (a) Find the deflection sensitivity in volts applied to the deflecting plates per millimetre deflection at the screen. (b) Find the density of a magnetic cross-field, extending over 50 mm of the beam path and distant 400 mm from the screen, that will give a deflection at the screen of 10 mm.
$[26.5 \times 10^6$ m/s; 2.67 V/mm; $0.8 \times 10^{-4}$ T]

**Problem 1.4**

The vertical distance between two horizontal flat plates in a vacuum is $x$. The potential difference between the plates is $v = V \sin \omega t$, and the lower plate is maintained at zero potential. At time $t = 0$ an electron at rest is released from the lower plate. Derive expressions for the subsequent velocity and position of the electron in relation to $\omega t$ and sketch these functions.

If $V = 25$ V, $\omega = 6 \times 10^7$ rad/s and $x = 100$ mm, calculate the kinetic energy and the distance of the electron from the lower plate in each case when $\omega t = \pi$, $3\pi/2$ and $2\pi$.
$[9.8 \times 10^{-19}$ J; $2.46 \times 10^{-19}$ J; 0 J; 38.4 mm; 70 mm; 76.8 mm]

**Problem 1.5**

A sinusoidal voltage of 4 V r.m.s. and frequency 10 MHz is applied to the electrodes of a parallel-plate capacitor in an evacuated space. The plates are 30 mm apart. An electron leaves one plate in a direction normal to the plate with a velocity of $2 \times 10^5$ m/s at an instant $t = 0$ when the potential difference is a maximum and the opposite plate is positive. Derive expressions for the velocity $v$ and the displacement $x$ of the electron at time $t$ and sketch the relationship between $v$ and $t$ and between $x$ and $t$.

Calculate the position and velocity of the electron when $t = 0.5 \times 10^{-7}$ s and estimate the time taken by the electron to reach the further plate.
$[2 \times 10^5 + 5.28 \times 10^5 \sin \omega t$ m/s; $2 \times 10^5 t + \dfrac{5.28}{200\pi} (1 - \cos \omega t)$ m; $v = 2 \times 10^5$ m/s; $x = 26.8$ mm; $t = 1.5 \times 10^{-7}$ s]

**Problem 1.6**

The anode and cathode of a diode are coaxial cylinders of radii $R$ and $r$, respectively, with $R > r$. A potential difference $V$ is maintained between them. An electron leaves the cathode radially with negligible velocity. Derive an expression for the subsequent velocity of the electron as a function of the radius $x$ from the axis of the cylinders. Show that the velocity reaches half of its final value when $x = (Rr^3)^{\frac{1}{4}}$. The effects of space charge are to be neglected.

**Problem 1.7**

An electron is accelerated through a potential difference $V$ and then enters a uniform magnetic field of magnetic flux density $\overline{B}$ in a direction perpendicular to the field. Show that the electron will describe a circular path, and derive an expression for the radius of the circle. If the flux density $\overline{B}$ is $10^{-3}$ T, and the electron

leaves the magnetic field 0.005 μs after entering it, calculate the angle between the direction of entry of the electron and its direction of leaving the field.
[129.6°]

## Problem 1.8

Two large parallel plates are spaced 5 mm apart in a vacuum, and a sinusoidal potential difference of $V \sin (\omega t + \phi)$ is maintained between the plates. An electron is injected into the interelectrode space at time $t = 0$, at an equal distance from the two plates, and with an initial velocity parallel to the plates. If the kinetic energy of the electron at $t = 0$ is 1500 eV and $\omega/2\pi$ is less than 1 MHz, calculate the maximum permissible value of $V$ for the electron not to hit either plate within the first 20 mm of its traverse, whatever the value of $\phi$.

(CEI Part 2)

[187.7]

## Problem 1.9

The separation between two parallel plates in a vacuum is $a$. One plate is maintained at zero potential and the other at $+V$ volts. There is a uniform magnetic field of flux density $\bar{B}$ T parallel with the plates. At time $t = 0$ an electron is released at zero velocity from the zero potential plate. Derive an expression for the velocity and for the direction of motion of the electron at time $t$.

If $a = 20$ mm, $V = 12$ V and $\bar{B} = 0.35$ mT, determine the point of impact of the electron on the positive plate, the transit time and the angle of incidence on impact.

(Leeds Polytechnic)

[9.26 mm for $x$; 0.021 s; 65.2°]

## Problem 1.10

In the diagram a constant magnetic flux density $\bar{B} = 1.5$ mT in an evacuated space acts parallel to the axis $O$–$Z$ and a constant electric field intensity $\bar{E} = 20$ kV/m acts in the negative direction parallel to $O$–$Y$, as shown. At time $t = 0$, an electron passes the origin $O$ with a velocity $u = 4 \times 10^6$ m/s in the direction $OY$. Derive expressions for the coordinates $x$ and $y$ of the position of the electron and time $t$, and calculate the maximum and minimum values of $y$ attained by the electron in its trajectory.

(IEE Part 3)

[$y_{max} = 10.2$ cm; $y_{min} = 0$]

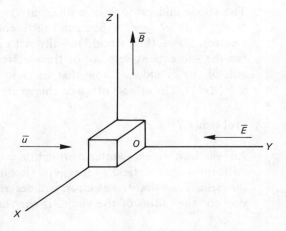

**Problem 1.11**

A charged particle of mass $m$ carrying a positive charge $q$ is initially at rest, in a vacuum in a uniform electromagnetic field comprising a static electric field of intensity $\bar{E}$ in the $x$-direction and a static magnetic flux density $\bar{B}$ in the $y$-direction. Neglecting gravitational force, develop the equations of motion of the particle in terms of $\bar{E}$ and $\bar{B}$. What is the maximum displacement in the $x$-direction from the rest position?

(CEI Part 2)

$$\left[ x_{\max} = \frac{2m\bar{E}}{q\bar{B}^2} \right]$$

**Problem 1.12**

A rectangular crossed-field system consists of a uniform electric field $\bar{E}_y$ perpendicular to a uniform magnetic field $\bar{B}_z$. An electron is injected into this system at velocity $u_x$. Derive an expression for the trajectory of the electron and, hence, find the value $u_{x0}$ of the injection velocity for which the trajectory of the electron is a straight line.

(CEI Part 2)

**Problem 1.13**

A particle carrying a charge $q$ travels with velocity $\bar{u}$ in a region occupied by an electric field of strength $\bar{E}$ and a magnetic field of flux density $\bar{B}$. Justify the expression

$$\bar{F} = q\,[\bar{E} + \bar{u} \times \bar{B}\,]$$

for the force exerted on the particle.

A stream of electrons passes through a hole in the lower of two metal plates, with a velocity $\bar{u}$ at an angle of 30° to the $y$-axis. The plates are a distance $s$ apart and are held at a p.d. $V$; the space between them is evacuated. Obtain an expression for the trajectory of the stream.

Given that $\bar{u} = 20 \times 10^6$ m/s and $s = 50$ mm, for what p.d. $V$ will the electrons just graze the upper plate, and at what distance from the hole will they again reach the lower plate?

(CEI Part 2)

$$\left[ y = 1.733x + 35.2 \times 10^{10} \times \frac{V}{s} \times \frac{x^2}{u^2}\,,\ 852\ \text{V};\ 11.55\ \text{cm} \right]$$

# 2 Electrostatic Field Theory

## 2.1 Fact Sheet

**(a) Coulomb's Law**

Two small sphere-like charged particles $q_1$, $q_2$ (whose radii are very small compared with the distance between them) are immersed in an insulating medium of permittivity $\epsilon$. The magnitude of the force of reaction between them is given by

$$\overline{F} = \frac{q_1}{4\pi} \times \frac{q_2}{\epsilon d^2} \ \text{N}$$

where $d$ is the distance between the particles.

**(b) Electric Fields**

*An electric field* may be defined as a region of space in which electrical charges experience forces.

**(c) Electric Intensity**

Electric intensity $\overline{E}$ (V/m), a vector quantity, is defined as the force experienced by a particle bearing unit positive charge, at the point under consideration from a point charge $q$:

$$\overline{E} = \frac{q \times 1}{4\pi\epsilon \ d^2} \ \text{V/m}$$

**(d) Superimposition Principle**

As the electric field is a linear function of the value of the charge, the fields of more than one point charge are linearly superpositionable by vector addition.

### (e) Gauss' Theorem and Electric Flux

Gauss' theorem states that when there is an electric flux through any closed surface surrounding an electrical charge, it equals the amount of charge enclosed by the surface:

$$\text{flux } \psi = q \text{ C}$$

### (f) Electric Flux Density

Electric flux density, $\overline{D}$ (C/m$^2$), is also a vector quantity, and is sometimes referred to as electric displacement. The integral of flux density $\overline{D}$ over a closed equipotential surface must be equal to the enclosed charge.

For a charged particle enclosed by an imaginary sphere of radius $d$ m,

$$\text{flux density at the sphere surface} = \frac{q}{4\pi d^2} \text{ C/m}^2$$

from which it can be seen that

$$\frac{\overline{D}}{\overline{E}} = \epsilon$$

### (g) Electric Potential

Electric potential, $V$ (volts), is a scalar quantity defined as the work done by extraneous forces against the forces of the electric field, in moving a particle bearing unit charge from one point to another at a constant velocity. The difference in potential between points X and Y is given by

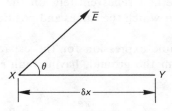

**Fig. 2.1**

$$\delta V = - \overline{E} \cos \theta \; \delta x$$

or

$$\frac{\delta V}{\delta x} = - \overline{E}_x$$

where $\overline{E}_x = \overline{E} \cos \theta$. In the limit, as $\delta x \to 0$,

$$\frac{\mathrm{d}V}{\mathrm{d}x} = - \overline{E}_x$$

or

$$V = - \int \overline{E}_x \cdot \mathrm{d}x \text{ V}$$

where $V$ is the potential at the point X, or the work that must be carried out in bringing a unit charge from infinity at zero potential at this point. The negative sign is an indication that the work done is against the electric field $\overline{E}$.

Remember that it is now possible to evaluate not only the electric field distribution of most conductor systems, but also the potential distribution and, hence, capacitance:

$$q = CV \quad \text{C}$$

### (h) Method of Images

The method of images is a method for solving electrostatic problems in which conducting boundary surfaces are present. Figure 2.2 shows area 1 containing two point charges $q_1$, $q_2$ and a conducting equipotential boundary surface separating it from area 2. It is possible to find a set of charges in area 2, $q_1'$, $q_2'$, $q_3'$ ..., so placed that when the physical boundary is removed, there is an exact similar equipotential $V$ formed by the system of charges and the field in area 1 remains unaltered.

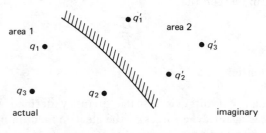

**Fig. 2.2**

The utility of this method relies entirely on the simplicity of the boundary surface and the ease with which the values and positions of the imaginary charges $q_1'$, $q_2'$ can be located.

For example, the simple expression for the capacitance of a pair of parallel conductors, isolated from the ground, having radii $r$ with a distance $D$ between centres,

$$C = \frac{\pi \epsilon}{\log_e (D - r)/r} \quad \text{F/m}$$

is not true when applied to a two-wire transmission line above earth, since the earth presents an easy path for the electric flux and so increases the capacitance.

### (i) Boundary Conditions

Boundary conditions are of the utmost importance in the study of electromagnetic fields.

#### (i) *Ideal Conductors*

1. The electric field strength $\overline{E}$ inside a conductor is zero.
2. The electric field strength $\overline{E}$ is external to the conductor and normal to the surface.

3. The surface of the conductor *must* be an equipotential.

$\oint \overline{E} \cdot \mathrm{d}l = 0$   loop integral of field strength
$\oint \overline{D} \cdot \mathrm{d}s = q$   Gaussian surface of electric flux density with free charges at the surface

$\overline{E}_t = 0, \overline{D}_t = 0$ and $\overline{D}_n \Delta s = \Delta q$.

$$\overline{D}_n = \frac{\Delta q}{\Delta s} = \rho_s$$

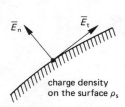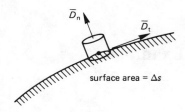

Fig. 2.3

### (ii) *Dielectric Boundaries*

Conditions at the boundary between two different dielectrics of permittivity $\epsilon_1$ and $\epsilon_2$.

1. The tangential electric field strength $\overline{E}_t$ undergoes no change in passing through the boundary and is said to be continuous at the boundary.
2. It follows that the electric flux density $\overline{D}_t$ is discontinuous at the boundary, where $\epsilon_1 \neq \epsilon_2$, since

$$\overline{E}_{t1} = \overline{E}_{t2} = \frac{\overline{D}_{t1}}{\epsilon_1} = \frac{\overline{D}_{t2}}{\epsilon_2}$$

from Gauss' theorem

$$\overline{D}_{n1} = \overline{D}_{n2} = \rho_s$$

as electric flux density $\overline{D}$ can only occur if there are *free* charges at the surface and these do not arise in normal dielectrics. Hence, $\rho_s = 0$, yielding

$$\overline{D}_{n1} = \overline{D}_{n2}$$

and

$$\frac{\overline{E}_{n1}}{\overline{E}_{n2}} = \frac{\epsilon_2}{\epsilon_1}$$

### (j) Energy Associated with the Electric Field

The problem of calculating the mechanical forces on bodies in electric fields could be carried out using Coulomb's law for each pair of charges and applying the superposition principle. However, it is found to be more expedient to calculate the energy of the system and deduce the forces from this result.

The energy of a group of charged conductors is *potential energy*, recovered when the system is discharged.

In any conductor system, the energy is given by

$$W = \tfrac{1}{2} \int \overline{D} \times \overline{E} \ \mathrm{d}v$$

the 'summation' being made for every volume element in the whole field:

$$W = \tfrac{1}{2} \epsilon \int \bar{E}^2 \ \mathrm{d}v$$

or

$$\frac{1}{2\epsilon} \int \bar{D}^2 \ \mathrm{d}v$$

## 2.2 Worked Examples

**Example 2.1**

Estimate the capacitance of an air capacitor formed from two conducting plates of area 0.12 m², spaced 8 mm apart.

The capacitance is unchanged when the separation of the plates is increased to 9.5 mm and a sheet of ebonite 2.5 mm thick is introduced between them. Estimate the capacitance when the ebonite is in position and the plate spacing is 8 mm.

(CEI Part 2)

**Solution 2.1**

Capacitance of parallel-plate capacitor is

$$\frac{\epsilon_0 \times \text{area of plates}}{\text{plate spacing}}$$

Therefore,

$$C = \frac{1 \times 0.12}{36\pi \times 10^9 \times 8 \times 10^{-3}} = 132.6 \text{ pF}$$

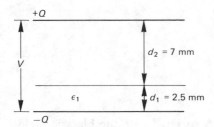

The next step is to calculate the relative permittivity $\epsilon_1$ of the ebonite. The method used is to evaluate the capacitance for the ebonite and the air section and, hence, the total capacitance for the two in series:

$$C_1 = \frac{A \, \epsilon_0 \, \epsilon_1}{d_1}$$

$$C_2 = \frac{A \, \epsilon_0}{d_2}$$

$$\text{total capacitance} \quad C = \frac{C_1 C_2}{C_1 + C_2}$$

$$= \frac{A \, \epsilon_0 \, \epsilon_1}{d_1 + d_2 \epsilon_1}$$

$$132.6 \times 10^{-12} = \frac{0.12 \times \epsilon_1}{36\pi \times 10^9 \, (2.5 + 7\epsilon_1) \times 10^{-3}}$$

Solving for $\epsilon_1$ yields $\epsilon_1 = 2.5$. Now the plate separation is reduced to 8 mm; hence, $d_2 = 5.5$ mm. Therefore,

$$\text{new capacitance} = \frac{0.12 \times 2.5 \times 10^3}{36\pi \times 10^9 \, (2.5 + 5.5 \times 2.5)} \quad \text{F}$$

$$= \underline{163.2 \text{ pF}}$$

**Example 2.2**

A capacitor is formed by two concentric spheres. Derive an expression for the capacitance in terms of the radii of the spheres and the permittivity of the medium between them.

If the radii are 500 and 100 mm, respectively, and there is a steady potential difference between the spheres of 100 kV, calculate the maximum value of the electric stress in the dielectric.

Assuming that the radius of the inner sphere may be varied, while the radius of the outer sphere and the potential difference are unchanged, determine the lowest value of the maximum stress which can be achieved and the radius of the inner sphere for which it occurs.

(IEE Part 3)

*Solution 2.2*

The Gaussian area for the spherical combination is $4\pi x^2$ m$^2$; therefore,

$$\text{electric intensity} \; \bar{E}_x = \frac{q}{4\pi\epsilon \, x^2} \; \text{V/m}$$

where $q$ C is the positive charge on the inner sphere. The potential difference between the spheres is $V$ volts, and is determined from

$$V = - \int \bar{E}_x \, \mathrm{d}x = - \frac{-q}{4\pi\epsilon} \int_b^a \frac{\mathrm{d}x}{x^2}$$

Therefore,

$$V = \frac{-q}{4\pi\epsilon} \left[ -\frac{1}{x} \right]_b^a = \frac{q}{4\pi\epsilon} \left[ \frac{1}{a} - \frac{1}{b} \right] \; \text{V}$$

where $a$ and $b$ are the radii of the two spheres.

$$\text{Capacitance} \; C = \frac{q}{V} = \frac{4\pi\epsilon}{\left[ \dfrac{1}{a} - \dfrac{1}{b} \right]} \; \text{F}$$

Therefore,

$$\bar{E}_x = \frac{V}{x^2 \left[ \dfrac{1}{a} - \dfrac{1}{b} \right]} \; \text{V/m}$$

and is a maximum when $x = a$:

$$\bar{E}_{max} = \frac{V}{a^2 \left[\dfrac{1}{a} - \dfrac{1}{b}\right]} \text{ V/m}$$

For the numerical values

$$\bar{E}_{max} = \frac{100}{10^2 \left[\dfrac{1}{10} - \dfrac{1}{50}\right]} = \underline{12.5 \text{ kV/cm}}$$

Rearrange the above equation for $\bar{E}_{max}$ to give

$$\bar{E}_{max} \left[a - \frac{a^2}{b}\right] = V$$

evaluate $d\bar{E}/da$ and equate the result to zero. This yields $2a = b$. $b = 500$ mm, so that

$$a = 250 \text{ mm}$$

and the minimum stress is

$$\bar{E}_{max} = \frac{100}{25^2 \left[\dfrac{1}{25} - \dfrac{1}{50}\right]} = \underline{8 \text{ kV/cm}}$$

## Example 2.3

Derive an expression for the capacitance per unit length of a single-core lead-sheathed cable with two layers of different dielectrics. Such a cable, designed to work at 66 kV to earth, has a conductor diameter of 10 mm. The relative permittivities of the two dielectrics are 4 and 2.5, respectively, with maximum working stress of 60 kV/cm² and 40 kV/cm², respectively. Calculate the minimum internal diameter under the lead sheath.

## *Solution 2.3*

Consider a charge $q$ C on the core conductor. Gauss' theorem gives the stress in the inner layer as

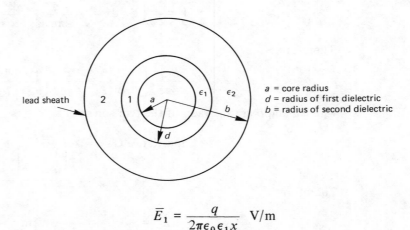

$$\bar{E}_1 = \frac{q}{2\pi\epsilon_0\epsilon_1 x} \text{ V/m}$$

for $a \leqslant x \leqslant d$, while in the outer layer

$$\bar{E}_2 = \frac{q}{2\pi\epsilon_0\epsilon_2 x} \ \text{V/m}$$

for $d \leqslant x \leqslant b$. If $V$ volts is the potential difference between the core conductor and sheath, then

$$V = -\int_d^a \bar{E}_1 \ dx - \int_b^d \bar{E}_2 \ dx \ \text{V}$$

$$= -\frac{q}{2\pi\epsilon_0}\left[\int_d^a \frac{dx}{\epsilon_1 x} + \int_b^d \frac{dx}{\epsilon_2 x}\right] \ \text{V}$$

$$= \frac{q}{2\pi\epsilon_0}\left[\frac{1}{\epsilon_1} \log_e \frac{d}{a} + \frac{1}{\epsilon_2} \log_e \frac{b}{d}\right] \text{V}$$

Capacitance per unit length is $q/V$ C/m.

$$C = \frac{2\pi\epsilon_0}{\left[\frac{1}{\epsilon_1} \log_e \frac{d}{a} + \frac{1}{\epsilon_2} \log_e \frac{b}{d}\right]} \ \text{F}$$

Maximum value of stress in layer 1 is

$$\bar{E}_{\max 1} = \frac{q}{2\pi\epsilon_0\epsilon_1 a}$$

or

$$\bar{E}_{\max 1} = \frac{V}{a\epsilon_1\left[\frac{1}{\epsilon_1} \log_e \frac{d}{a} + \frac{1}{\epsilon_2} \log_e \frac{b}{d}\right]}$$

Similarly,

$$\bar{E}_{\max 2} = \frac{V}{d\epsilon_2\left[\frac{1}{\epsilon_1} \log_e \frac{d}{a} + \frac{1}{\epsilon_2} \log_e \frac{b}{d}\right]}$$

Combining these two expressions,

$$\frac{\bar{E}_{\max 1}}{\bar{E}_{\max 2}} = \frac{d\epsilon_2}{a\epsilon_1}$$

$a = 5$ mm; therefore,

$$d = \frac{5 \times 4 \times 60}{2.5 \times 40} = 12 \ \text{mm}$$

Therefore,

$$\frac{1}{4} \log_e \frac{12}{5} + \frac{1}{2.5} \log_e \frac{b}{12} = \frac{66}{5 \times 4 \times 60 \times 10^{-1}} = 0.55$$

$$\frac{1}{2.5} \log_e \frac{b}{12} = 0.55 - \frac{1}{4} \times 0.8755$$

$$\log_e \frac{b}{12} = 2.5 \times 0.331 = 0.8278$$

$$\frac{b}{12} = 2.288$$

$$b = 27.46$$

internal sheath diameter = $\underline{54.92 \ \text{mm}}$

**Example 2.4**

The lower plate of the parallel-plate capacitor shown in the diagram is fixed, and the upper plate is attached to a spring of stiffness $k$. With the capacitor uncharged,

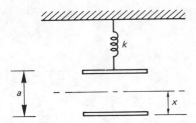

the plate separation is $a$. Find an expression for the maximum voltage $V_{max}$ and the corresponding separation, $x$, for which the plate is in stable equilibrium with a finite separation of the plates.

(CEI Part 2)

*Solution 2.4*

Assume that the plate area is 1 m$^2$, so that

$$\text{electrostatic force} = q\,\overline{E} = CV \times \frac{V}{x} \text{ N}$$

$$C = \frac{\epsilon \times 1}{x}$$

Therefore,

$$\overline{F}_s = \frac{\epsilon V^2}{x^2} \text{ N}$$

The force developed by the spring $\overline{F}_m = k\,(a - x)$ N. Equilibrium will occur when these two forces are equal. The diagram shows the relationship between force and distance for both $\overline{F}_s$ (at different voltages) and $\overline{F}_m$, which has a linear response.

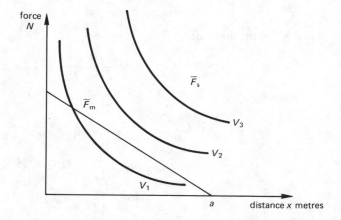

The slope for the spring law is $-k$, while the slope for the electrostatic law is $d\overline{F}_s/dx$ and to obtain the value of $V_{max}$ equate these two relationships:

$$\frac{d\overline{F}_s}{dx} = -\frac{2\epsilon V_{max}^2}{x^3} = -k$$

Thus,

$$V_{max}^2 = \frac{kx^3}{2\epsilon}$$

$$V_{max} = \left[\frac{kx^3}{2\epsilon}\right]^{\frac{1}{2}}$$

and

$$x = \sqrt[3]{\frac{2\epsilon V_{max}^2}{k}}$$

Now the two forces are equal at this point, when the distance is $x_1$, say. Therefore,

$$k(a - x_1) = \frac{\epsilon V_{max}^2}{x_1^2} = \frac{kx_1^3}{2x_1^2} = \frac{kx_1}{2}$$

$$a - x_1 = \frac{x_1}{2}$$

or

$$a = \frac{3x_1}{2}$$

Therefore,

$$V_{max} = \left[\frac{k \times 8 \times a^3}{2 \times \epsilon \times 27}\right]^{\frac{1}{2}} = 0.38 \left[\frac{ka^3}{\epsilon}\right]^{\frac{1}{2}}$$

## Example 2.5

A point charge $Q$ is placed within an earthed hollow conducting sphere of radius $R$ at a distance $d$ from the centre, as shown in the diagram. Find the direction of

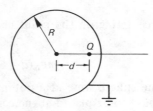

the force experienced by the charge, and obtain an expression for its magnitude in terms of $Q, R$ and $d$.

(CEI Part 2)

## Solution 2.5

If the surface of the sphere is taken to be at zero potential, then the field outside the sphere is due to the charge $Q$, and an image point charge $-Q'$ distance $x$ from the centre of the sphere on a line joining the centre of the sphere to the point charge.
Using the diagram,

$$\text{potential at } P = \frac{Q}{4\pi\epsilon_0 r} - \frac{Q'}{4\pi\epsilon_0 r'} = 0$$

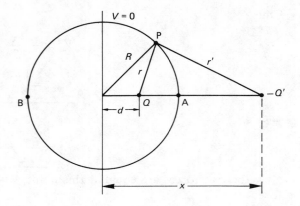

then

$$Q' = \frac{Qr'}{r}$$

It is necessary that $r'/r$ is constant at all points on the sphere; two particular points are at A and B on the line joining the two point charges.

$$\frac{r'}{r} = \frac{R - x}{d - R} = \frac{R + x}{R + d}$$

Solving this equation yields $x = R^2/d$. Therefore,

$$\frac{r'}{r} = \frac{R}{d}$$

and

$$Q' = \frac{QR}{d}$$

The force acting on the point charge $Q$ is towards the sphere shell and is given by

$$\overline{F} = \frac{Q \times Q'}{4\pi\epsilon_0(d - x)^2} = \frac{Q^2 \times R \times d}{4\pi \times \epsilon_0 \times (d^2 - R^2)^2} \text{ N}$$

[If the sphere were at a potential $V$, an additional image charge $Q'' = 4\pi\epsilon_0 RV$ would have to be placed at the centre of the sphere.]

## Example 2.6

A circular loop, of radius $r$, of thin wire in a vacuum carries a total charge $q$ which is uniformly distributed. Derive an expression for the electric field strength at any point along the axis of the loop.

An infinite conducting sheet is now placed parallel to the plane of the loop, and 50 mm from it. If $q = 0.01$ $\mu$C and $r = 100$ mm, calculate the potential between the centre of the loop and the sheet.

(IEE Part 3)

**Solution 2.6**

$$\text{Line density } \rho = \frac{q}{2\pi r} \text{ c/m}$$

Thus,

$$\overline{E}_x = \frac{\rho \, dl}{4\pi\epsilon_0 h^2} \text{ V/m}$$

considering $\rho \, dl$ as a point charge.

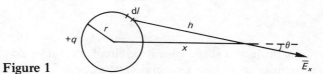

**Figure 1**

The axis component $\overline{E} = \overline{E}_x \cos\theta$, while for the whole loop, the length $dl$ becomes $2\pi r$. Therefore,

$$\overline{E} = \frac{\rho \times 2\pi r \times \cos\theta}{4\pi\epsilon_0 h^2} \text{ V/m}$$

or

$$\overline{E} = \frac{q \cos\theta}{4\pi\epsilon_0 h^2} = \frac{qx}{4\pi\epsilon_0 h^3} \text{ V/m}$$

$$\overline{E} = \frac{qx}{4\pi\epsilon_0 (x^2 + r^2)^{\frac{3}{2}}} \text{ V/m}$$

At the point P in Figure 2 the total electric field strength is given by

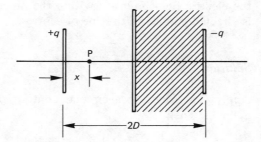

**Figure 2**

$$\frac{qx}{4\pi\epsilon_0 (x^2 + r^2)^{\frac{3}{2}}} + \frac{q(2D - x)}{4\pi\epsilon_0 [(2D - x)^2 + r^2]^{\frac{3}{2}}}$$

by means of the introduction of an image loop with charge $-q$.

$$\text{Potential difference } V = -\int_{2D}^{0} \overline{E} \, dx$$

$$V = \frac{-q}{4\pi\epsilon_0} \left[ \frac{-1}{(x^2 + r^2)^{\frac{1}{2}}} + \frac{1}{[(2D - x)^2 + r^2]^{\frac{1}{2}}} \right]_{2D}^{0}$$

$$= \frac{q}{4\pi\epsilon_0} \left[ \frac{1}{r} - \frac{1}{[4D^2 + r^2]^{\frac{1}{2}}} - \frac{1}{[4D^2 + r^2]^{\frac{1}{2}}} + \frac{1}{r} \right] \text{ V}$$

$$= \frac{q}{2\pi\epsilon_0} \left[ \frac{1}{r} - \frac{1}{[4D^2 + r^2]^{\frac{1}{2}}} \right] \text{ V}$$

The potential difference between the centre of the loop and the sheet is half this value of $V$ — that is,

$$\frac{q}{4\pi\epsilon_0}\left[\frac{1}{r} - \frac{1}{[4D^2 + r^2]^{\frac{1}{2}}}\right]\text{V}$$

For the numerical part,

$$\text{potential difference} = \frac{0.01 \times 10^{-6} \times 36\pi \times 10^9}{4\pi}\left[\frac{10^2}{10} - \frac{10^2}{(200)^{\frac{1}{2}}}\right]\text{V}$$

$$= \underline{264\ \text{V}}$$

### Example 2.7

A region in the shape of a long circular cylinder contains a uniform space charge of density $q$. Derive a general expression for the electric field intensity $\bar{E}$ within the region and remote from the ends.

Two long parallel non-conducting cylinders having the configuration shown in the diagram contain between them a uniform space-charge density $q$. Show that

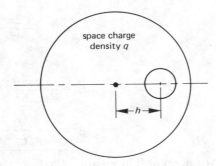

space charge
density $q$

$\leftarrow h \rightarrow$

the electric field intensity within the inner cylinder is everywhere the same, and is directed parallel to the line of centres.

(CEI Part 2)

### Solution 2.7

Apply Gauss' law to a circular contour of radius $r$ centred on the axis of the cylinder. Then

$$\bar{D} \times 2\pi r \times 1 = \text{charge enclosed} = q\pi r^2 \text{ (for 1 m length)}$$

thus

$$\bar{D} = \frac{qr}{2}$$

so that

$$\underline{\bar{E} = \frac{qr}{2\epsilon}}$$

($\bar{E}$ acts radially outwards for positive charge.)

Using the principle of superposition, consider a point with coordinates $x$ and $y$ within the inner cylinder so that, owing to $+q$ filling the outer cylinder shown in the diagram,

$$\bar{E}_x = \frac{qx}{2\epsilon_0}$$

34

and

$$\overline{E}_y = \frac{qy}{2\epsilon_0}$$

while, owing to $-q$ filling the inner cylinder,

$$\overline{E}_x = \frac{q(h-x)}{2\epsilon_0}$$

and

$$\overline{E}_y = -\frac{qy}{2\epsilon_0}$$

Thus, the field intensity due to both cylinders with space charge $q$ between them is

$$\overline{E}_x = \frac{qh}{2\epsilon_0}$$

and

$$\overline{E}_y = 0$$

Hence, electric field intensity has the same value and is parallel to the line of centres.


**Example 2.8**

A parallel-plate capacitor is formed by two large conducting plates spaced by distance $2d$. A dielectric material of permittivity $\epsilon = \epsilon_0 \epsilon_r$ is deposited on one of the plates to a thickness $d$. The remainder of the space is filled with a negative space charge of uniform volume density $\rho$. The two plates are maintained at the same potential. Derive expressions for the surface density of the free charges on the plates as shown in the diagram.

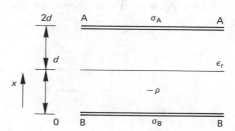

*Solution 2.8*

$$0 \leqslant x \leqslant d; \ \overline{D}_x = \sigma_B - \rho x; \ \text{and} \ \overline{E}_x = \frac{\overline{D}_x}{\epsilon_0}$$

$$d \leqslant x \leqslant 2d; \ \overline{D}_x = \sigma_B - \rho d; \ \text{and} \ \overline{E}_x = \frac{\overline{D}_x}{\epsilon_0 \epsilon_r}$$

Now $V_{AB} = 0$; therefore,

$$-\int_0^{2d} \overline{E}_x \, dx = 0$$

Thus,

$$\int_0^d \frac{(\sigma_B - \rho x)\,\mathrm{d}x}{\epsilon_0} + \int_d^{2d} \frac{(\sigma_B - \rho d)\,\mathrm{d}x}{\epsilon_0 \epsilon_r} = 0$$

$$\left[\sigma_B x - \tfrac{1}{2}\rho x^2\right]_0^d + \frac{1}{\epsilon_r}\left[\sigma_B x - \rho d x\right]_d^{2d} = 0$$

$$\sigma_B d - \tfrac{1}{2}\rho d^2 + \frac{\sigma_B 2d}{\epsilon_r} - \frac{\rho 2 d^2}{\epsilon_r} - \frac{\sigma_B d}{\epsilon_r} + \frac{\rho d^2}{\epsilon_r} = 0$$

$$\sigma_B\left[1 + \frac{1}{\epsilon_r}\right] = \rho d\left[\frac{1}{2} + \frac{1}{\epsilon_r}\right]$$

$$\underline{\sigma_B = \frac{\rho d}{2}\frac{[\epsilon_r + 2]}{[\epsilon_r + 1]}}$$

Now

$$\sigma_B - \rho d + \sigma_A = 0$$

Therefore,

$$\underline{\sigma_A = \rho d - \rho d\,\frac{[\epsilon_r + 2]}{[\epsilon_r + 1]} = \frac{\rho d \epsilon_r}{2[\epsilon_r + 1]}}$$

## Example 2.9

Derive an expression for the capacitance of a two-wire line above earth using the method of images.

*Solution 2.9*

The conductors A and B are of equal radii $r$ distance $d$ apart and $q$ C/m of charge per unit length of conductor is considered. By the principle of images, the electric field above ground will be the same as if the earth were absent and two other conductors A' and B', as shown in the diagram, reflections of A and B, were present.

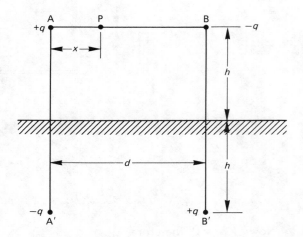

The potential difference between A and B is $V$ volts, equal to $(q/\pi\epsilon_0)\log_e (d - r)/r$, ignoring the images.

At the point P

$$\text{electric intensity } \bar{E}_{A'P} = \frac{-q}{2\pi\epsilon_0 [4h^2 + x^2]^{\frac{1}{2}}}$$

The component in the direction A to B is

$$\bar{E}_{AP} \cos \angle APA' = \bar{E}_A$$

or

$$\bar{E}_{A'} = \frac{-q}{2\pi\epsilon_0 [4h^2 + x^2]^{\frac{1}{2}}} \times \frac{x}{[4h^2 + x^2]^{\frac{1}{2}}}$$

$$= \frac{-qx}{2\pi\epsilon_0 [4h^2 + x^2]}$$

A similar component due to conductor B' is

$$\bar{E}_{B'} = \frac{-q}{2\pi\epsilon_0} \frac{[d-x]}{[4h^2 + (d-x)^2]}$$

Total potential difference due to these imaginary conductors is

$$V' = -\int_{d-r}^{r} (\bar{E}_{A'} + \bar{E}_{B'}) \, dx$$

$$= \frac{q}{2\pi\epsilon_0}\left[\int_{d-r}^{r} \frac{x \, dx}{4h^2 + x^2} + \int_{d-r}^{r} \frac{(d-x)\, dx}{4h^2 + (d-x)^2}\right]$$

$$= \frac{q}{2\pi\epsilon_0}\left[\tfrac{1}{2}\log_e (4h^2 + x^2) - \tfrac{1}{2}\log_e (4h^2 + (d-x)^2)\right]_{d-r}^{r}$$

$$= \frac{q}{2\pi\epsilon_0}\log_e \left[\frac{4h^2 + r^2}{4h^2 + (d-r)^2}\right]$$

$$= \frac{-q}{2\pi\epsilon_0}\log_e \left[\frac{4h^2 + (d-r)^2}{4h^2 + r^2}\right]$$

Total potential difference between conductors A and B is

$$\frac{q}{\pi\epsilon_0}\log_e \frac{d}{r} - \frac{q}{2\pi\epsilon_0}\log_e \left[\frac{4h^2 + (d-r)^2}{4h^2 + r^2}\right]$$

$$= \frac{q}{2\pi\epsilon_0}\left[\log_e \frac{d^2}{r^2} - \log_e \frac{4h^2 + (d-r)^2}{4h^2 + r^2}\right]$$

$$\text{The equivalent capacitance} = \frac{2\pi\epsilon_0}{\log_e \dfrac{d^2}{r^2} - \log_e \dfrac{4h^2 + (d-r)^2}{4h^2 + r^2}}$$

### Example 2.10

A long straight cylindrical wire, of radius $r$, in a medium of permittivity $\epsilon$, is parallel to a horizontal plane conducting sheet. The axis of the wire is at a distance $h$ above the sheet. Derive an expression for the capacitance per unit length between the wire and the plane, stating any assumptions made.

The potential difference between the wire and the sheet is 5 kV, with $r = 2$ mm and $h = 100$ mm. Calculate the electric stress in the medium at the upper surface of the sheet (a) vertically below the wire; (b) at a point 200 mm from the axis of the wire.

### Solution 2.10

Assume $h \geqslant r$ and the conducting sheet to be infinitely large, as shown in the diagram. The introduction of the image does not distend the field of the real charge.

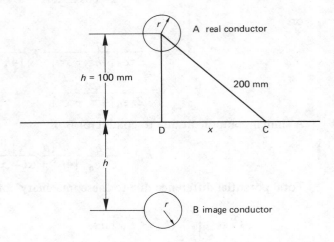

Evaluate the potential difference between A and B:

$$\bar{E}_x = \frac{q}{2\pi\epsilon_x} - \frac{(-q)}{2\pi\epsilon\,(2h-x)} \quad \text{V/m}$$

where $q$ C/m is the charge per metre length of conductor

$$V = -\int_{2h-r}^{r} \bar{E}_x \; \mathrm{d}x = \frac{-q}{2\pi\epsilon} \int_{2h-r}^{r} \frac{\mathrm{d}x}{x} + \frac{\mathrm{d}x}{2h-x} \quad \text{V}$$

$$= \frac{-q}{2\pi\epsilon} \left[ \log_e x - \log_e (2h-x) \right]_{2h-r}^{r} \quad \text{V}$$

$$= \frac{q}{\pi\epsilon} \log_e \frac{2h-r}{r} \quad \text{V}$$

$V_{\text{AD}}$ = potential difference to the plane conducting sheet and is given by

$$V_{\text{AD}} = \frac{q}{2\pi\epsilon} \log_e \frac{2h-r}{r}$$

$$\text{Capacitance per unit length} = \frac{2\pi\epsilon}{\log_e \dfrac{(2h-r)}{r}} \quad \text{F/m}$$

The charge on the conductor is

$$q = \frac{5000 \times 2\pi}{36\pi \times 10^9 \times \epsilon_r \times \log_e \dfrac{(20-0.2)}{0.2}} \quad \text{C/m}$$

Assuming $\epsilon_r = 1$, then $q = 0.06 \; \mu$C per metre length:

(a) $\bar{E}_{\text{AD}} = \dfrac{0.06 \times 10^{-6} \times 36\pi \times 10^9}{\pi \times 10 \times 10^{-2}} \quad \text{V/m}$

$$= \underline{21.6 \text{ kV/m}}$$

(b) $\bar{E}_{AC} = \dfrac{qh}{\pi\epsilon_0\,(h^2 + x^2)}\left(\text{angle } \sin^{-1}\dfrac{h}{(h^2 + x^2)^{\frac{1}{2}}}\right)$

$\qquad = \dfrac{0.06 \times 10^{-6} \times 10 \times 10^{-2} \times 10^4 \times 36\pi \times 10^9}{\pi\,(100 + 300)}$ V/m

$\qquad = \underline{5.4\ \text{kV/m}}$

**Example 2.11**

Two parallel sheets of plate glass mounted vertically are separated by a uniform air-gap between their inner surfaces. The sheets, suitably sealed round the outer edges, are immersed in oil. A uniform electric field in a horizontal direction exists in the oil. The strength of the electric field in the oil is 1 kV/m and the relative permittivities of the glass and oil, respectively, are 6.0 and 2.5. Calculate from first principles the magnitude and direction of the electric field strength in the glass and in the enclosed air, respectively, when (a) the direction of the field in the oil is normal to the glass surfaces, and (b) the direction of the field in the oil makes an angle of 60° with a normal to the glass surface. Neglect edge effects.

(IEE Part 3)

*Solution 2.11*

Apply Gauss' theorem to the extremely small cylinder ABCD which encloses part of the boundary.

If there are no charges on the surface, then the net outward flux must be zero, and as AB → 0, the flux through the curved surface of the cylinder does not exist.

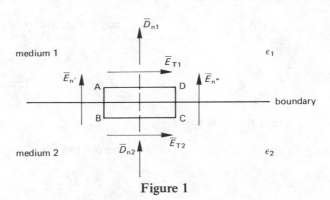

**Figure 1**

Normal components of the flux density must be equal

$$\bar{D}_{N1} = \bar{D}_{N2}$$

The voltage round a closed path is zero:

$$\oint \bar{E}\ dx = -\,\bar{E}_{n1}\,AB + \bar{E}_{T2}\,BC + \bar{E}_{n11}\,CD - \bar{E}_{T1}\,DA = 0$$

as AB → 0. Therefore, $\qquad\qquad \bar{E}_{T1} = \bar{E}_{T2}$

Now $\qquad\qquad\qquad\qquad\quad \bar{D}_1 = \epsilon_1 \bar{E}_1$

and $\qquad\qquad\qquad\qquad\quad \bar{D}_2 = \epsilon_2 \bar{E}_2$

Apply the boundary conditions to the vectors in Figure 2.

$$\bar{D}_1 \cos\alpha = \bar{D}_2 \cos\beta$$

$$\bar{E}_1 \sin\alpha = \bar{E}_2 \sin\beta$$

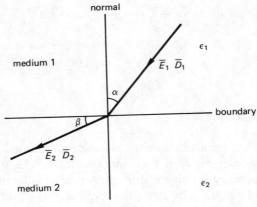

**Figure 2**

Therefore,

$$\frac{\epsilon_1}{\epsilon_2} = \frac{\tan \alpha}{\tan \beta}$$

(a) $\epsilon_1 = 2.5$, $\epsilon_2 = 6$, $\epsilon_3 = 1$ for oil, glass and water, respectively. $\alpha = \beta = 90°$.

$$\bar{E}_2 = 1000 \, \frac{2.5}{6} \; \text{V/m} = \underline{416.7 \; \text{V/m}}$$

$$\bar{E}_3 = 416.7 \times \frac{6}{1} = \underline{2500 \; \text{V/m}}$$

from oil to glass.

(b)
$$\tan \beta = \tan 60° \times \frac{6}{2.5}$$

$$\beta = 76.5°$$

$$\bar{E}_2 = \frac{1000 \times \sin 60°}{\sin 76.5°} = \underline{890.6 \; \text{V/m glass}}$$

from the glass to air

$$\tan \beta = \tan 76.5° \times \frac{1}{6}$$

$$\beta = 34.8°$$

$$\bar{E}_3 = \frac{890.6 \times \sin 76.5°}{\sin 34.8°} \; \text{V/m} = \underline{1517.5 \; \text{V/m}}$$

**Example 2.12**

An air capacitor comprises two concentric thin-walled metal spheres, respectively of radius $R$ (outer) and $r$ (inner).

(i) Derive an expression for the mutual capacitance of the system and use it to show that the capacitance of a single isolated sphere is proportional to its radius.

(ii) If $R$ is fixed and $r$ can be varied, show that when a voltage $V$ is applied between the spheres, the maximum electric stress in the air dielectric is at least $4V/R$.

(iii) Determine the total capacitance to earth of the outer sphere when the inner sphere is earthed.

(CEI Part 2)

**Solution 2.12**

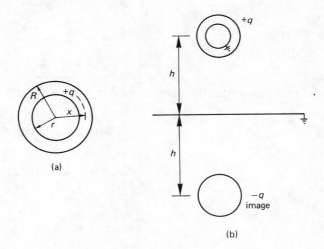

(a)

(b)

Consider part (a) of the diagram. The flux density at any radius $x$ is

Hence,
$$\bar{D}_x = \frac{q}{4\pi x^2} \ \text{C/m}^2$$

electric intensity $\bar{E}_x = \dfrac{q}{4\pi\epsilon_0 x^2} \ \text{V/m}$

Therefore,
$$V = -\int \bar{E}_x \ \mathrm{d}x = \frac{q}{4\pi\epsilon_0} \int_R^r \frac{\mathrm{d}x}{x^2}$$

$$V = -\frac{q}{4\pi\epsilon_0} \left[ -\frac{1}{x} \right]_R^r = \frac{q}{4\pi\epsilon_0} \left[ \frac{1}{r} - \frac{1}{R} \right] \text{V}$$

(i)  Mutual capacitance $C = \dfrac{4\pi\epsilon_0}{\left[ \dfrac{1}{r} - \dfrac{1}{R} \right]} \ \text{F}$

If $R \to \infty$, then $C \to 4\pi\epsilon_0 r$ — i.e. capacitance of a single sphere is proportional to its radius. From the expression

$$\bar{E}_x = \frac{q}{4\pi\epsilon_0 x^2}$$

and

$$V = \frac{q}{4\pi\epsilon_0} \left[ \frac{1}{r} - \frac{1}{R} \right]$$

then, by substitution,

$$\bar{E}_{\max} = \frac{rRV}{r^2(R-r)} = \frac{RV}{r(R-r)}$$

$$\frac{\mathrm{d}\bar{E}_{\max}}{\mathrm{d}r} = \frac{(rR - r^2) \times 0 - RV(R - 2r)}{(rR - r^2)^2} = 0$$

Therefore, $2r = R$.

41

(ii) $\bar{E}_{max} = \dfrac{RV}{\dfrac{R}{2}\left(R - \dfrac{R}{2}\right)} = \dfrac{RV}{\dfrac{R^2}{4}}$

Hence,

$$\bar{E}_{max} \geqslant \frac{4V}{R}$$

From part (b) of the diagram an image sphere is considered:

$$V = -\int_{2h-R}^{R} \frac{q\,dx}{4\pi\epsilon_0 x^2} + \frac{q\,dx}{4\pi\epsilon_0(2h-x)^2}$$

$$V = -\frac{q}{4\pi\epsilon_0}\left[-\frac{1}{x} + \frac{1}{2h-x}\right]_{2h-R}^{R}$$

$$V = -\frac{q}{4\pi\epsilon_0}\left[-\frac{1}{R} + \frac{1}{2h-R} + \frac{1}{2h-R} - \frac{1}{R}\right] \text{ V}$$

$$= \frac{q}{2\pi\epsilon_0}\left[\frac{1}{R} - \frac{1}{2h-R}\right] \text{ V}$$

Potential difference between the sphere and earth $= \dfrac{q}{4\pi\epsilon_0}\left[\dfrac{1}{R} - \dfrac{1}{2h-R}\right]$ V

Capacitance to earth $= \dfrac{4\pi\epsilon_0}{\left[\dfrac{1}{R} - \dfrac{1}{2h-R}\right]}$ F

## 2.3  Unworked Problems

### Problem 2.1

A standard air capacitor for use with a high-voltage Schering bridge has a capacitance of 80 pF and consists of a vertical cylindrical working electrode mounted concentrically inside a longer cylinder. End effects are eliminated by inner guard electrodes. The length of the working electrode is 1000 mm and the inside radius of the outer cylinder is 400 mm. The sinusoidal applied voltage is 100 kV (r.m.s.). Calculate the radius of the working electrode and the peak electric stress at its surface.

If the capacitor has a power factor of 0.0001 at 50 Hz and its equivalent circuit is represented by a pure capacitance in series with a resistance, calculate the series resistance.

Sketch the electric field distribution at the lower end of the capacitor and use the diagram to explain the function of the guard electrodes.

(IEE Part 3)

[$a$ = 200 mm; 10.19 kV/cm; 4 kΩ]

### Problem 2.2

A long cylindrical single-core cable has a conductor of radius 5 mm and an earthed metal sheath of inner radius 12.5 mm. The insulant comprises two dielectrics, of equal radial thickness but with different permittivities. If the maximum electric field strength is to be the same in the two dielectrics, determine (a) the ratio of the permittivities, and (b) the maximum electric field strength for a voltage of 100 kV r.m.s.

Sketch the radial distribution of the electric field and of the voltage to earth.

On what property of the insulant would the electric field distribution depend if the cable were operated on a direct instead of an alternating voltage?

(CEI Part 2)

[(a) 1.75:1; (b) 169 kV/cm]

### Problem 2.3

A parallel-plate air capacitor, of plate area $A$, and spacing $s$, is connected permanently across the terminals of an electrometer, the capacitance of which is related to its terminal voltage $V$ by the expression $C = K + aV^2$, where $K$ and $a$ are constants. The combination is charged to a potential difference $V_1$ and then isolated. When a dielectric slab of area $A$ and thickness $d$ (with $d < s$) is fully inserted between the plates of the capacitor, the electrometer indication changes to $V_2$. Neglecting fringing, find an expression for the relative permittivity of the slab. Will $V_2$ be greater or less than $V_1$?

(CEI Part 2)

$$\left[ \frac{1}{\epsilon_r} = \frac{A\epsilon_0}{d\left[\dfrac{V_1^2}{V_2^2}(C + K + aV_1^2) - (K + aV_2^2)\right]} - \frac{s}{d} + 1; V_2 < V_1 \right]$$

### Problem 2.4

A long cylindrical conductor of radius 20 mm and at a potential of 250 kV lies with its axis parallel to and 0.1 m above a large plane earthed conductor. Find the potential and the potential gradient at a point mid-way between the centre of the conductor and the plane.

(CEI Part 2)

[214 kV; 3000 kV/m]

### Problem 2.5

In a geoelectric survey a current of 250 mA is fed into a spike thrust into the ground, and taken out from another spike 100 m away. Taking the current spikes to be equivalent to hemispherical electrodes of radius 0.1 m, find the p.d. necessary to drive the current through the earth path, if the ground has a uniform resistivity of 80 $\Omega$m.

Two potential spikes are driven into the ground on the line joining the current spikes, and set symmetrically between them 20 m apart. Find the potential difference between the potential spikes.

Obtain an expression for finding the resistivity of the earth with such a measuring arrangement, taking the electrode geometry as fixed.

(CEI Part 2)

[63.6 V; 0.053 V]

### Problem 2.6

The diagram shows the essential dimensions of a cylindrical air capacitor with its lower end immersed in oil of relative permittivity 2.0 and density 900 kg/m³. When a potential difference $V$ is applied to the capacitor, the oil level within it

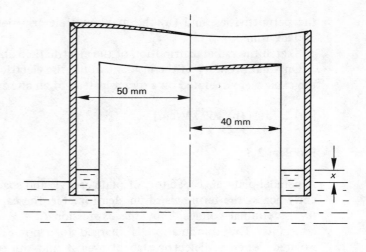

rises to a height $x$. Given that the breakdown stress of air is 3 MV/m, calculate the maximum possible value of $x$ and the corresponding voltage $V$.

(Eng. C)

[23 cm; 26.8 kV]

## Problem 2.7

A parallel-plate capacitor, with separation $s$, stores energy $W$ when the p.d. between the plates is $V$. Use the energy conservation principle to show that the force $f$ tending to reduce the plate separation is

$$f = - \left[ \frac{\partial W}{\partial S} \right]_{V=\text{constant}}$$

The air capacitor of the diagram is partly filled by a dielectric block of relative permittivity $\epsilon_r > 1$, and a constant p.d. $V$ is applied to the plates. Neglecting field fringing, show

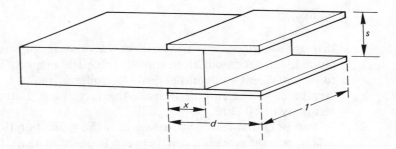

  (i) that the force $f_1$ of attraction between the plates increases with increase of $x$;
 (ii) that there is a force $f_2$ on the dielectric block tending to increase $x$; and
(iii) that $f_2/(df_1/dx) = s$.

(CEI Part 2)

## Problem 2.8

Show that the capacitance $C$ between two conductors immersed in a medium of absolute permittivity $\epsilon$, and the resistance between the same conductors when immersed in a medium of resistivity $\rho$, are related by $CR = \epsilon\rho$. Hence explain how an electrolyte tank or a surface-conducting paper sheet can be used to assess the capacitance of a conductor system.

The shapes of the cross-sections of the inner and outer conductors of an air-filled coaxial cable are silver-painted on to conducting paper. The resistance between the two painted loops is 500 $\Omega$, and the resistance between opposite edges of a square of the paper is 3000 $\Omega$. Determine the capacitance per metre length of the cable. If the core and sheath were concentric circles, what would be the ratio of their radii?

(CEI Part 2)

$$\left[ C = \frac{10^{-9}}{6\pi} \text{ F}; \ \frac{b}{a} = 2.85 \right]$$

## Problem 2.9

Discuss the principles underlying the method of images applied to field problems.

A point charge $q$ lies between two parallel infinite conducting planes, each at earth potential and with a separation $d$. Show that the force experienced by the charge is

$$f = \frac{q^2 d (b-a)}{16\pi\epsilon_0} \sum_{n=0}^{\infty} \frac{1+2n}{[ab + n(n+1)d^2]^2}$$

where $a$ and $b$ are the distances between the charge and the planes, with $a + b = d$.

Determine the limiting value of the force when the charge lies very close to one of the planes.

(CEI Part 2)

$[f \rightarrow \infty \text{ as } a \rightarrow 0]$

## Problem 2.10

The flat surfaces of two dielectric materials 1 and 2, respectively of absolute permittivity $\epsilon_1$ and $\epsilon_2$, are in close contact. A static electric field of strength $\overline{E}_1$ in 1 is directed towards the interface at an angle $\alpha_1$ to the normal. The field strength $\overline{E}_2$ in 2 makes the angle $\alpha_2$ to the normal. There is no free charge on the interface.
 (a)  Show that the tangential components of $\overline{E}_1$ and $\overline{E}_2$ are equal, and that the normal components of electric flux density $\overline{D}_1$ and $\overline{D}_2$ are equal.
 (b)  Obtain expressions for $\overline{E}_2$ and $\alpha_2$ in terms of $\overline{E}_1$ and $\alpha_1$.
 A spherical globule of water ($\epsilon$ large) lies in oil ($\epsilon$ small) in an electric field. Sketch the form of the electric field pattern in and around the globule.

(CEI Part 2)

## Problem 2.11

Describe what happens to an uncharged conductor when it is placed in a static electric field. The diagram shows three long air-filled concentric conducting cylinders, respectively of radii $a$, $b$ and $c$, set parallel to an extensive plane earth with their common axis at a distance $d$ from the plane, where $d \geqslant c$. The middle cylinder is earthed by a wire which is assumed to have no effect on the electric field distribution. Derive expressions for the capacitance per unit length between the cylinders, and between the outer cylinder and the earth plane.

For the condition when charges of $+Q$ and $-Q$ per unit length are placed respectively on the inner and outer cylinders, (i) determine an expression for the

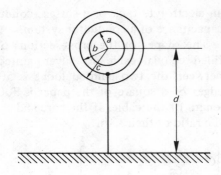

total charge $Q_m$ per unit length on the middle cylinder, and (ii) show that $Q_m$ approaches zero as $d$ approaches infinity.

(CEI Part 2)

$$\left[ C_1 = \frac{2\pi\epsilon_0}{\log_e b/a} \; ; \; C_3 = \frac{2\pi\epsilon_0}{\log_e c/b} \; ; \; C_4 = \frac{2\pi\epsilon_0}{\log_e 2d/c} \; ; \; -Q + \frac{QC_3}{C_4 + C_3} \right]$$

## Problem 2.12

Explain what is meant by *space charge*. Discuss the effect of space charge on the conduction in a planar diode.

Show (a) that the average velocity of an electron in a space-charge-limited diode is one-third of the maximum; and (b) that in the absence of space charge the average velocity is one-half of the maximum. Assume in each case that the initial velocity of the electron is zero.

(CEI Part 2)

## Problem 2.13

In the diagram A and B are two long air-insulated conductors of small diameter in a plane normal to that of the page. The mutual capacitance of the pair of conductors is 6 pF per metre length and the distance between centres is $\sqrt{3}$ m. The steady potential difference between the conductors is 10 kV and the direct current carried by the two conductors, in opposite directions, respectively, is 100 A.

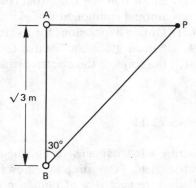

Calculate the magnitude and direction of the electric and magnetic field strengths at point P. Conductor A is positive with respect to B, and carries current downwards into the page.

(IEE)

[935 V/m; 30° to AP; 13.8 A/m along PB]

**Problem 2.14**

Discuss briefly the analogy between the following field systems:
  (a) A current between electrodes immersed in a conducting medium.
  (b) An electric field established by a potential difference between two elect-rodes embedded in a dielectric medium.
  (c) A magnetic flux crossing a gap between two magnetised iron surfaces.

Point out the comparable quantities, and indicate any difference or assumptions.

Find an expression for the capacitance per unit length between two concentric cylinders.

Using the result, find the resistance between two copper electrodes comprising a disc of radius 20 mm centrally within an annular ring of inner radius 100 mm, both hard-soldered to the surface of a sheet of manganim 0.5 mm thick and of resistivity 0.5 $\mu\Omega$ m.

[0.256 m$\Omega$]

**Problem 2.15**

Derive an expression for the mutual capacitance for a pair of parallel overhead lines: the conductors are of equal radii $r$, distance $d$ apart and carry $q$ C/m of charge per unit length of conductor.

$$\left[ \pi\epsilon_0 / \log_e \frac{d-r}{r} \text{ F} \right]$$

**Problem 2.16**

A capacitor with air as dielectric consists of a long metal rod of radius $a$ along the axis of a long metal tube of inside radius $b$. A steady p.d. $V$ is applied between the electrodes. Derive expressions for the capacitance per unit length and for the electric stress in the air at radius $x$.

Estimate the effective radius of the inner electrode and the effective capacit-ance per metre length when $V$ = 60 kV, $a$ = 5 mm, $b$ = 100 mm, the breakdown strength of air is 30 kV/cm and the effect of corona is to produce a uniform con-ducting layer round the rod.

If the same effective capacitance is to be obtained without corona by wrapping the rod with a dielectric of relative permittivity 2.0, find the thickness of dielectric required and the corresponding maximum stress in the air.

$$\left[ \frac{2\pi\epsilon_0}{\log_e \frac{b}{a}} \text{ F} \cdot \frac{V}{x \log_e \frac{b}{a}} ; 7.85 \text{ mm}; 21.83 \text{ pF/m}; 7.33 \text{ mm}; 19.12 \text{ kV/cm} \right]$$

**Problem 2.17**

State in integral and differential forms, Gauss' law relating the electric flux density $\overline{D}$ at a point to the volume charge density $\rho$.

Two infinite parallel conducting sheets A and B, separated by a distance $2d$, are maintained at the same potential. Sheet A is coated to a thickness $d$ by a homo-geneous and isotropic dielectric material of relative permittivity $\epsilon_r$ = 2.0. The space between the dielectric and sheet B has a space charge of uniform density $\rho$. Stating clearly any assumptions made, determine the surface charge densities on A and B.

(CEI Part 2)

$$\left[ \sigma_A = - \frac{1}{3} \rho d; \ \sigma_B = - \frac{2}{3} \rho d \right]$$

# 3 Electromagnetic Theory

## 3.1  Fact Sheet

As the forces on electrically charged particles are associated with an electric field, so the forces on magnets can be ascribed to a magnetic field.

A *unit pole* may be defined as that magnetic pole which experiences a unit force of one newton when situated in a magnetic field of unit intensity.

*Magnetic potential* can be evaluated from the unit pole concept. The space derivative of magnetic potential gives the *magnetic intensity* of the field

$$\bar{H} = - \text{ grad } \Omega = - \nabla\Omega$$

A difference in magnetic potential between two points a and b may be related to the line integral of the vector $\bar{H}$; then

$$\Omega = \Omega_b - \Omega_a = - \int_a^b \bar{H} \, dx \text{ A}$$

In this line integral the path must always be taken in such a manner that it does not link with any current.

If the integration is taken around a closed loop, starting and ending at the same point, the value of the line integral is *not* zero.

### (a)  Magnetic Work Law

The value of the line integral of $\bar{H}$ taken *once* around the circuit is called the magnetomotive force (m.m.f.). Thus,

$$\oint \bar{H} \, dx = \text{m.m.f. A}$$

If the circuit carries conduction current $i$, then

$$\text{m.m.f.} = i \text{ A}$$

and if the current is carried by a winding of $n$ turns of wire, then

$$\text{m.m.f.} = \oint \bar{H} \, dx = i \times n \text{ A}$$

i.e. the line integral of $\bar{H}$ around any closed path is equal to the current linked with the path.

### (b)  Biot–Savart Law

The magnetising force at a point P due to current $i$ flowing in a circuit is considered the same as if each element $\delta l$ of the whole circuit (see Figure 3.1) contributed a vector $\delta\bar{H}$ and is given by

$$\delta\bar{H} = \frac{i \, \delta l \sin\theta}{4\pi r^2} \text{ A/m}$$

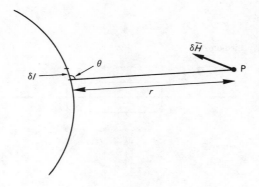

**Fig. 3.1**

The direction of $\delta\bar{H}$ is normal to both the plane of $\delta l$ and radius vector $r$.

The total magnetising force $\bar{H}$ is obtained from

$$\oint \frac{i\,\delta l\sin\theta}{4\pi r^2}\ \text{A/m}$$

### (c) Faraday's Law

Energy can be transferred from one circuit to another, not connected to the first, through magnetic flux linkage. The two circuits are then said to be magnetically coupled. The basis of this magnetic action is Faraday's law of electromagnetic induction:

$$\text{e.m.f.} = \oint \bar{E}\ \text{d}s = -\frac{\partial\phi}{\partial t}$$

that is, a voltage is induced in a closed circuit when the magnetic flux linking with the circuit is changed; the induced e.m.f. is always in such a direction as to oppose the flux change.

### (d) Method of Images

As in the case of the electric field theory, it is possible to solve certain types of problem by the creation of image current-carrying conductors and satisfying the boundary conditions at the air–iron surface.

#### (i) *Boundary Conditions*

At the boundary between two different media, the magnetic field may change abruptly both in magnitude and direction. The normal component of flux density is continuous across the boundary between the two media:

$$\bar{B}_{N1} = \bar{B}_{N2}$$

The integral of magnetic intensity around a closed path is equal to the enclosed current:

$$\oint \bar{H}\ \text{d}x = [\bar{H}_{N1}\ ab + \bar{H}_{T1}\ ad - \bar{H}_{N11}\ dc - \bar{H}_{T2}\ bc] = 0$$

as $ab \rightarrow 0$,

$$\bar{H}_{T1} = \bar{H}_{T2}$$

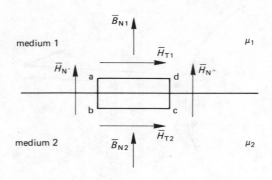

**Fig. 3.2**

i.e. tangential components of magnetic force are continuous across the boundary between the two media, provided that the boundary has no current sheet.


### (e) Energy Associated with the Magnetic Field

The potential energy of a circuit, in its simplest form (current × flux), enables the calculation of the mechanical force acting on each element of circuit to be made.

Moving a circuit in a certain direction by a distance $\delta x$ and if the resultant force in the same direction is $\overline{F}_x$, the potential energy diminishes by $\overline{F}_x \, \delta x$. Therefore,

$$\overline{F}_x = i \, \frac{\delta \phi}{\delta x}$$

Suppose that a current-carrying circuit deforms as a result of the electromagnetic forces set up by its own field; then the deformation will always be such that the flux linkage increases, so that the stored energy is greater after the deformation.

Assuming the current to be constant (energy supplied = work done + increase in stored energy),

$$i\delta\phi = \text{work done} + \tfrac{1}{2} \, i \, \delta\phi$$

Therefore,

$$\text{work done} = \tfrac{1}{2} \, i \, \delta\phi$$

$$\overline{F}_x \times \delta x = \tfrac{1}{2} \, i \, \delta\phi$$

$$\overline{F}_x = \tfrac{1}{2} \, i \, \frac{\delta\phi}{\delta x}$$

If the circuit through which the current flows has a self-inductance $L$, then

$$iL = \phi$$

Therefore,

$$i \, \delta L = \delta\phi$$

and

$$\overline{F}_x = \tfrac{1}{2} \, i^2 \, \frac{\partial L}{\partial x}$$

## 3.2  Worked Examples

### Example 3.1

A long fluid conductor of circular cross-section, radius $R$ and magnetic permeability $\mu$ carries an electric current $i$. Assuming a uniform current density in the conductor, show that the electromagnetically produced hydrostatic pressure at a point in the conductor distant $r$ from the axis is

$$\frac{\mu\, i^2\, [R^2 - r^2]}{4\pi^2\, R^4}$$

A gaseous conductor has a radius of 50 mm when the current is 200 kA. Calculate the pressure at the centre of the conductor.

### Solution 3.1

From the diagram below, the current density $J = i/\pi R^2$; therefore inside any radius $r$

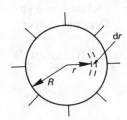

$$\text{current} = \frac{i}{\pi R^2} \times \pi r^2 = \frac{i\, r^2}{R^2}\ \text{A}$$

$$\text{magnetising force } \bar{H}_\mathrm{r} = \frac{i\, r^2}{R^2} \times \frac{1}{2\pi r}$$

$$= \frac{i\, r}{2\pi R^2}\ \text{A/m}$$

The corresponding flux density $\bar{B}_\mathrm{r} = \dfrac{\mu i r}{2\pi R^2}$  T

Change in hydrostatic pressure is equal to force per unit area per metre length of conductor:

$$\frac{\mathrm{d}P}{\mathrm{d}r} = \frac{\text{magnetic force}}{\pi R^2} = \bar{B} J$$

$$= \frac{\bar{B}_\mathrm{r}}{\pi} \times \frac{i}{R^2}$$

$$= \frac{\mu \times i^2 \times r}{2 \times \pi^2 \times R^4}$$

$$\mathrm{d}P = \frac{\mu \times i^2 \times r \times \mathrm{d}r}{2 \times \pi^2 \times R^4}$$

$$P = \int_r^R \frac{\mu \times i^2 \times r \times \mathrm{d}r}{2 \times \pi^2 \times R^4} = \frac{\mu \times i^2}{2 \times \pi^2 \times R^4}\left[\frac{r^2}{2}\right]_r^R$$

$$P = \frac{\mu \times i^2}{4 \times \pi^2 \times R^4}\ [R^2 - r^2]\ \text{N/m}^2\ \text{(Pa)}$$

Numerically, when $r = 0$,

$$P = \frac{4\pi \times (200)^2 \times 10^6 \times 10^4}{10^7 \times 4 \times \pi^2 \times 25}\ \text{N/m}^2\ \text{(Pa)}$$

$$P = \frac{4 \times 10^7}{25 \times \pi} \times \frac{1}{9.81}\ \text{kg/m}^2$$

$$P = 0.519 \times 10^5\ \text{kg/m}^2$$

**Example 3.2**

A radial magnetic field of average density 0.1 T is maintained in the air-gap between two concentric vertical iron cylinders, as shown in the diagram. A copper ring, placed symmetrically in the gap, is released and falls through the magnetic field. Derive the equation of motion of the ring, assuming $a \ll r$.

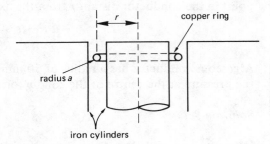

Calculate (a) the velocity of the ring at time $t = 15$ ms after its release, and (b) the terminal velocity. [For copper, resistivity $\rho = 1.68 \times 10^{-8}$ Ωm and density $\delta = 7800$ kg/m$^3$].

(CEI Part 2)

**Solution 3.2**

When the ring falls, an e.m.f. will be induced in it, with a value of $\bar{B} \times 2\pi r \times v$. This, in turn, will generate a current $i$ = e.m.f./resistance.

$$\text{Resistance of copper ring} = \frac{\rho l}{A} \ \Omega$$

or

$$R = \frac{\rho \times 2\pi r}{\pi a^2} \ \Omega$$

Thus,

$$i = \frac{\bar{B} \times v}{\rho} \times \pi a^2 \ \text{A}$$

A current-carrying conductor in a magnetic field means that the ring is subjected to a retarding force of $\bar{B} \times 2\pi r \times i$ and is also subjected to an accelerating force due to gravity. Thus,

$$m \frac{\mathrm{d}v}{\mathrm{d}t} = mg - \bar{B} \times 2\pi r \times i$$

where $m$ is the mass of the ring and is equal to $(2\pi r)(\pi a^2 \delta)$ or $2\pi^2 r a^2 \delta$ (mass = volume × density).

From the above equation,

$$\frac{\mathrm{d}v}{\mathrm{d}t} + \frac{\bar{B} \times (2\pi r) \times \bar{B} \times v \times (\pi a^2)}{\rho \times 2\pi^2 r a^2 \delta} = g$$

or

$$\frac{\mathrm{d}v}{\mathrm{d}t} + \frac{\bar{B}^2 v}{\rho \delta} = g$$

Substitute the numerical data:

$$\frac{dv}{dt} + \frac{0.01\,v}{1.68 \times 10^{-8} \times 7800} = 9.81$$

$$\frac{dv}{dt} + 76.3\,v = 9.81$$

This equation has to be solved — use the $s$ notation (Laplace)

$$s\bar{v} + 76.3\,\bar{v} = \frac{9.81}{s}$$

or

$$\bar{v} = \frac{9.81}{s\,(s + 76.3)}$$

Transform from Laplace tables to yield

$$v\,(t) = 0.129\,(1 - e^{-76.3t})$$

At $t = 15$ ms

$$v\,(t) = 0.129\,(1 - e^{-1.145})$$

(a)  $\underline{v\,(t) = 0.088 \text{ m/s}}$

(b)  $\underline{\text{terminal velocity} = 0.129 \text{ m/s}}$

**Example 3.3**

(a) A small circular loop of radius $r$ carrying a current $I$ is in the same plane as, and at the centre of, a large circular loop of radius $R$, where $R \gg r$. Show that the magnetic vector potential at a point on the circumference of the large loop is $A = \mu_0 I\,(r/2R)^2$.

(b) Using the result in (a), or otherwise, calculate the e.m.f. induced in the large loop when the current in the small loop is $I \cos \omega t$.

(CEI Part 2)

**Solution 3.3**

$$A = -\int \bar{E}\,\partial t$$

direction is that of $\bar{E}$, or

$$\bar{E} = -\frac{\partial \bar{A}}{\partial t}$$

$$\bar{E}\,\delta l = -\frac{\partial \bar{A}}{\partial t}\,\delta l$$

$$\oint \bar{E}\,\delta l = -\oint \frac{\partial \bar{A}}{\partial t}\,\delta l = -\frac{\partial \Phi}{\partial t} \text{ V}$$

Thus,

$$\oint \bar{A}\,\delta l = \Phi \text{ Wb}$$

or

$$\frac{1}{s}\oint \bar{A}\,\delta l = \frac{\Phi}{s} = \bar{B} \text{ T}$$

where $s$ is an area around the loop of radius $r$.

As the line integral of $\overline{A}$ around any closed circuit is equal to the magnetic flux linked by the circuit, the flux density on the axis due to the current $I$ at a radius $R$ from the small loop is given by

$$\text{flux density } \overline{B} = \frac{\mu_0 I}{2R} \text{ T}$$

This statement is possible since $R \gg r$.

$$\text{Flux linking the small loop} = \frac{\mu_0 I}{2R} \times \pi r^2$$

The path around the large loop $= 2\pi R$; therefore,

$$\overline{A} \times 2\pi R = \frac{\mu_0 I}{2R} \cdot \pi r^2$$

$$\overline{A} = \mu_0 I \left(\frac{r}{2R}\right)^2$$

(b) From the above,

$$\overline{E} = \frac{\mathrm{d}\overline{A}}{\mathrm{d}t} = \mu_0 I \, \omega \sin \omega t \times \left[\frac{r}{2R}\right]^2$$

$$\oint \overline{E} \, \mathrm{d}l = -\frac{\mathrm{d}\Phi}{\mathrm{d}t} = \text{induced e.m.f.}$$

Thus,

$$\text{e.m.f.} = 2\pi R \, \mu_0 I \, \omega \sin \omega t \left[\frac{r}{2R}\right]^2$$

since $\omega = 2\pi f$, where $f$ is the current frequency.

$$\text{e.m.f.} = \mu_0 I f \sin \omega t \times R \left[\frac{\pi r}{R}\right]^2$$

$$= \frac{\mu_0 I f}{R} (\pi r)^2 \sin \omega t \text{ V}$$

### Example 3.4

Derive an expression for the magnetic field strength at any point on the axis of a single-turn loop carrying a steady current $I$: (a) when the loop is in the form of a circle of radius $r$, and (b) when it is square, with sides each of length $2a$.

Show that if the circle and the square have the same area, the respective field strengths at the centres of the loops are in the ratio $(\pi^3/32)^{1/2}$.

### Solution 3.4

In this problem start by using the Biot–Savart law to find the field strength at any point on the axis of a coil, as shown in Figure 1:

$$\delta \overline{H} = \frac{I \, \delta r \sin \theta}{4\pi l^2}$$

But in this example $\delta r = 2\pi r$ and $\theta = 90°$, considering the whole coil; therefore,

$$\overline{H} = \frac{I \times 2\pi r \times \sin 90°}{4\pi l^2} = \frac{I \, r}{2(r^2 + h^2)^{\frac{1}{2}}}$$

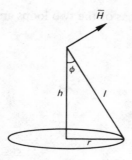

**Figure 1**

$$\text{Axial component } \overline{H}_c = H \sin \phi = \frac{Ir^2}{2l^3} = \frac{Ir^2}{2(r^2 + h^2)^{\frac{3}{2}}}$$

For a short conductor, obtain the field strength at a point directly over the centre of the conductor, as shown in Figure 2(a); Figures 2(b) and 2(c) show the square of side $2a$ from two different angles.

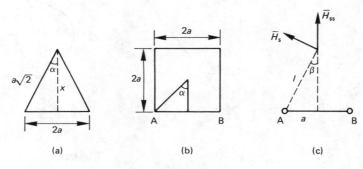

**Figure 2**

$$\text{Therefore} \quad \overline{H}_s = \frac{I}{4\pi a} \times 2 \sin \alpha = \frac{I}{4\pi a} \times 2 \times \frac{a}{a\sqrt{2}} = \frac{I\sqrt{2}}{4\pi a}$$

Applying this result to the square (Figure 2c),

$$\overline{H}_{ss} = \frac{I\sqrt{2}}{4\pi a} \times 4 \times \sin \beta = \frac{I\sqrt{2}}{\pi a} \times \frac{a}{l} = \frac{I\sqrt{2}}{\pi l} = \frac{I\sqrt{2}}{\pi (a^2 + h^2)^{\frac{1}{2}}}$$

Area of the circle $= \pi r^2$. At the centre $l = r$ or $h = 0$. Hence,

$$\overline{H}_{cc} = \frac{I}{2r}$$

Area of the square $= 4a^2$. At the centre $l = a$ or $h = 0$. Hence,

$$\overline{H}_{sc} = \frac{\sqrt{2}I}{\pi a}$$

Thus, the ratio of

$$\frac{\overline{H}_{cc}}{\overline{H}_{sc}} = \frac{I}{2r} \times \frac{\pi a}{\sqrt{2}I} = \frac{\pi a}{2\sqrt{2}r}$$

and the areas of the two loops are equal:

$$\pi r^2 = 4a^2$$

or

$$r = \frac{2a}{\sqrt{\pi}}$$

Therefore,

$$\frac{\bar{H}_{cc}}{\bar{H}_{sc}} = \frac{\pi a}{2\sqrt{2}} \times \frac{\sqrt{\pi}}{2a} = \left[\frac{\pi^3}{32}\right]^{\frac{1}{2}}$$

## Example 3.5

Develop an expression for the magnetic flux density at point P due to a steady current $I$ in each of the coplanar conductor configurations (a) and (b) of Figure 1. The conductors are situated in air.

(CEI Part 2)

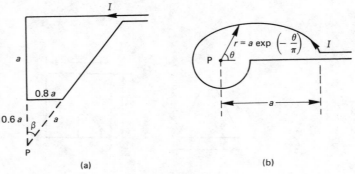

(a)                                    (b)

**Figure 1**

## Solution 3.5

(a) For a short conductor, with the point P perpendicularly opposite the current-carrying conductor,

$$\bar{H} = \frac{I}{4\pi d} \times \sin \beta$$

where $d$ is the perpendicular distance. For the conductor furthest away from P,

$$\bar{H} = \frac{I}{4\pi \times 1.6a} \times 0.8 = \frac{I}{8\pi a}$$

while, for the conductor nearest to P,

$$\bar{H} = \frac{I}{4\pi \times 0.6a} \times 0.8 = \frac{1.6 I}{8\pi \times 0.6a}$$

Therefore,

$$\bar{H}_P = \frac{I}{8\pi a} \left[\frac{1.6}{0.6} - 1\right] = \frac{I}{4.8\pi a}$$

and

$$\text{flux density } \bar{B}_P = \frac{4\pi}{10^7} \times \frac{I}{4.8\pi a} = \frac{0.833I}{a \times 10^7} \text{ T}$$

56

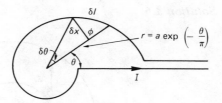

Figure 2

(b) Apply the Biot–Savart law to Figure 1(b), which is redrawn to show the method of solution in Figure 2:

$$r\delta\theta = \delta l \sin \phi$$

since

$$\frac{\delta x}{r} \doteq \delta\theta$$

and

$$\frac{\delta x}{\delta l} = \sin \phi$$

Now

$$\delta\bar{H} = \frac{I\,\delta l \sin \phi}{4\pi r^2} = \frac{Ir\delta\theta}{4\pi r^2}$$

$$= \frac{I\,\mathrm{d}\theta}{4\pi r} = \frac{I\,\mathrm{d}\theta}{4\pi\, a \exp\left[-\dfrac{\theta}{\pi}\right]}$$

Therefore,

$$\bar{H} = \int_0^{2\pi} \delta H = \frac{I}{4\pi a} \int_0^{2\pi} \frac{\mathrm{d}\theta}{\exp\left(-\dfrac{\theta}{\pi}\right)}$$

$$= \frac{I\pi}{4\pi a} \left[ \exp\left(+\frac{\theta}{\pi}\right) \right]_0^{2\pi}$$

$$= \frac{I}{4\pi} \left[ e^2 - 1 \right] = \frac{1.6\,I}{a}$$

Hence,

$$\text{flux density } \bar{B} = \frac{4\pi}{10^7} \times \frac{1.6\,I}{a} = \frac{2I}{a} \ \mu\mathrm{T}$$

## Example 3.6

The copper tube that forms the outer conductor of a concentric cable has a mean diameter of 5 mm and is 1 mm thick. If the cable is not to burst, what is the maximum current that it can carry during a short-circuit test? The ultimate strength of copper is 200 GPa.

(CEI Part 2)

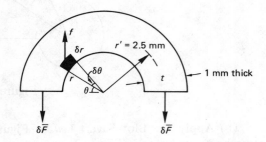

The flux density at the inner surface of the outer conductor shown in the diagram is a maximum — i.e.

$$\overline{B}_{max} = \frac{4\pi}{10^7} \times \frac{I_{max}}{2\pi \times 2 \times 10^{-3}} = \frac{I_{max}}{10^4} \text{ T}$$

while the flux density at the outer edge is zero. Therefore, the force on each element of area of outer conductor varies from a maximum at the inner edge to zero at the outer edge.

$$\text{Area of shaded section} = r\,\delta\theta \times \delta r$$

$$\text{Total segment area of outer conductor} = 2\pi r' t$$

$$= 2\pi \times 2.5 \times 10^{-3} \times 10^{-3}$$

$$= 5\pi \times 10^{-6}$$

Assume that the current is uniformly distributed (no skin effect); then the current in the element is

$$\delta i = \frac{r\,\delta\theta\,\delta r}{2\pi r'\,t} I_{max}$$

$$\delta i = \frac{2 \times 10^{-3} \times \delta\theta \times \delta r \times I_{max}}{5\pi \times 10^{-6}}$$

$$= \frac{\delta\theta\,\delta r\,I_{max} \times 10^3}{2.5\,\pi}$$

$$\text{Radial force on this element per unit length of conductor} = \overline{B}\delta i$$

$$\text{Vertical component } \overline{\delta}f = \overline{B}\delta i \sin\theta$$

$$= \frac{I_{max}}{10^4} \times \frac{\delta\theta \times \delta r \times I_{max} \times 10^3 \times \sin\theta}{2.5\,\pi}$$

$$= \frac{I_{max}^2\,\delta r \sin\theta\,\delta\theta}{25\,\pi}$$

$$2\overline{\delta}F = \frac{I_{max}^2\,\delta r}{25\,\pi} \int_0^\pi \sin\theta\,\delta\theta$$

$$\overline{\delta}F = \frac{I_{max}^2\,\delta r}{25\,\pi}$$

$$\text{Stress on this thin shell} = \frac{\overline{\delta}F}{\delta r \times 1} = \frac{I_{max}^2}{25\,\pi}$$

But the ultimate strength of the copper is $200 \times 10^9$. Therefore,

$$I_{max}^2 = 25\pi \times 200 \times 10^9$$

$$\underline{I_{max} = 3.96 \text{ MA}}$$

### Example 3.7

The three conductors of a transmission line are supported at points which form the vertices of an equilateral triangle RYB of side 1 m, RY being vertical. At a certain instant the currents in conductors R and Y are both 120 A, with the return current of 240 A in conductor B. Find the mechanical force on conductor B, giving both magnitude and direction.

(IEE Part 3)

### Solution 3.7

The conductor arrangement is shown in the diagram, with the appropriate forces.

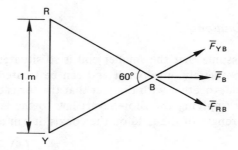

In the simplest form the force $\overline{F}$ acting on a current-carrying conductor of $I$ A and conductor length $l$, when lying in a magnetic field of flux density $\overline{B}$ T, is given by

$$\overline{F} = \overline{B} \times l \times I \text{ N}$$

The flux density $\overline{B}$ associated with a current-carrying conductor is found from

$$\overline{B} = \frac{\mu I}{2\pi d} \text{ T}$$

where $\mu$ is the absolute permittivity of the medium and $d$ is the perpendicular distance from the conductor. Applying this to the problem,

$$\overline{F}_{YB} = \frac{\mu_0 \, I_Y \, I_B}{2\pi \times \text{YB}} \text{ N/m}$$

$$= \frac{4\pi \times 120 \times 120}{10^7 \times 2\pi \times 1} \text{ N/m}$$

$$= 5.76 \times 10^{-3} \text{ N/m}$$

Similarly, $\overline{F}_{RB} = 5.76 \times 10^{-3}$ N/m

Both forces act as shown in the diagram; therefore,

$$\overline{F}_B = 2 \times 5.76 \times 10^{-3} \times \cos 30° = 9.88 \text{ N/m}$$

<u>horizontally away from conductors R and Y</u>

**Example 3.8**

Derive an expression for the mutual force between two coaxial circular coils of radii $R_1$, $R_2$, turns $N_1$, $N_2$ and currents $I_1$, $I_2$, respectively, if the distance between their centres is $L$, as shown in the diagram.

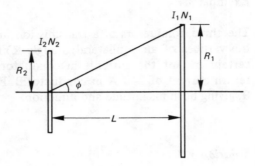

**Solution 3.8**

Assume that the smaller coil is so situated that the flux set up by the larger coil completely envelops it and can be treated as uniform over the area of the smaller coil, together with the fact that the turns of each coil are coplanar.

Applying the Biot–Savart law to the larger coil, in order to find the magnetic strength of the field on the coaxis, it can be seen that

$$\bar{H}_1 = \frac{I_1 N_1 \sin \phi \, R_1}{2\,(R_1^2 + L^2)}$$

and, since

$$\sin \phi = \frac{R_1}{(R_1^2 + L^2)^{\frac{1}{2}}}$$

$$\bar{H}_1 = \frac{I_1 N_1 R_1^2}{2(R_1^2 + L^2)^{\frac{3}{2}}}$$

Thus,

$$\text{flux density } \bar{B}_1 = \mu_0 \bar{H}_1 = \frac{\mu_0 I_1 N_1 R_1^2}{2(R_1^2 + L^2)^{\frac{3}{2}}}$$

Hence,

$$\text{flux linking the small coil } \Phi_2 = \pi R_2^2 \, \bar{B}_1$$

$$\text{flux linkage with coil 2} = \Phi_2 \, N_2$$

The mutual inductance between the coils is

$$M_{12} = \frac{\text{flux linkage with coil 2}}{\text{current of coil 1}}$$

$$= \frac{\pi R_2^2 \, \mu_0 I_1 N_1 R_1^2 N_2}{2(R_1^2 + L^2)^{\frac{3}{2}} I_1}$$

$$= \frac{\mu_0 \pi N_1 N_2 R_1^2 R_2^2}{2(R_1^2 + L^2)^{\frac{3}{2}}}$$

Since the potential energy of one circuit in the field of another is given by $M_{12} I_1 I_2$ (energy = force × distance),

$$\text{force between the coils} = I_1 I_2 \ \frac{dM_{12}}{dL}$$

$$F = \frac{3\mu_0 \pi N_1 N_2 R_1^2 R_2^2 I_1 I_2 L}{2(R_1^2 + L^2)^{\frac{5}{2}}} \ \text{N}$$

**Example 3.9**

Show, by the use of the method of images, how to obtain the complete magnetic field pattern associated with a current-carrying conductor situated near an air–iron boundary.

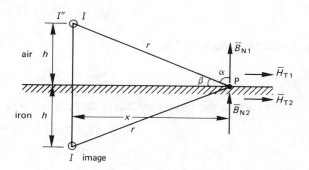

The iron is assumed to have a uniform finite permeability $\mu$. The conductor is parallel to the boundary, with current flowing out of the paper. The diagram shows an image conductor carrying $I'$ situated a distance $h$ below the boundary as shown, and a second image conductor $I''$ alongside the real conductor.

(LP)

**Solution 3.9**

*On the air side* the field is created by $I$ and $I'$, both assumed to be in air. *On the iron side* the field is due to currents $I$ and $I''$, both assumed to be in iron. Finally, the magnitude and direction of the currents in the image conductors must be such as to satisfy the boundary air–iron conditions.

At the point P on the media boundary

$$H_I = \frac{I}{2\pi r} \ \text{A/m}$$

and

$$H_{I'} = \frac{I'}{2\pi r} \ \text{A/m}$$

On the air side, the tangential component of the magnetising force is given by

$$H_{T1} = \frac{h}{2\pi r^2} \ (I - I')$$

$$\cos \alpha = \frac{h}{r}$$

(note the currents in the same direction, yielding opposing forces). On the iron side, since

$$H_I'' = \frac{I''}{2\pi r}$$

$$H_{T2} = \frac{h}{2\pi r^2} (I + I'')$$

(currents assumed to be in opposite directions). But at the boundary

$$H_{T1} = H_{T2}$$

Therefore,

$$I' = -I''$$

(image currents flow in opposite directions).

Now consider the normal components of flux density. On the air side

$$B_{N1} = \frac{\mu_0 x}{2\pi r^2} (I + I') \text{ T}$$

On the iron side

$$B_{N2} = \frac{\mu x}{2\pi r^2} (I + I'') \text{ T}$$

But across the boundary $B_{N1} = B_{N2}$ ; therefore,

$$\mu_0 (I + I') = \mu(I + I'') = \mu(I - I')$$

or

$$I' = \left[\frac{\mu - \mu_0}{\mu + \mu_0}\right] I \text{ for air}$$

While

$$I'' = -\left[\frac{\mu - \mu_0}{\mu + \mu_0}\right] I \text{ for iron}$$

If the iron has a high permeability, $\mu \gg \mu_0$, the field on the *air side* is that of two parallel conductors with nearly equal currents flowing in the same direction, situated in air, while on the *iron side* the field is that due to two coincident conductors ($I$ and $I''$) with the currents flowing in opposite directions, all situated in iron. The diagram shows a typical pattern.

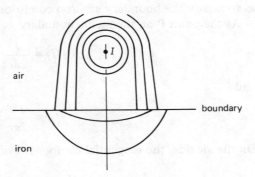

**Example 3.10**

Draw the system of images which, with the current in a long straight conductor buried in (but insulated from) an iron mass as shown in Figure 1, will closely represent the magnetic field of the current.

62

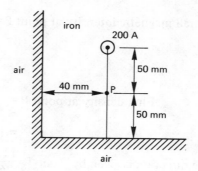

Figure 1

Estimate the flux density at point P and its direction, taking the relative permeability of the iron to be constant at 1000.

(CEI Part 2)

*Solution 3.10*

For a long thin single conductor, the magnetic intensity $\bar{H}$ is given by $I/2\pi x$ A/m acting at right angles to the radial length $x$.

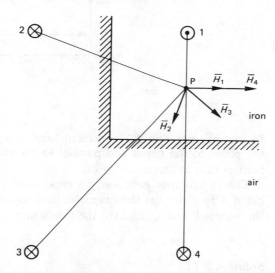

Figure 2

From Figure 1, the effect in the air of a conductor buried in the iron will be to replace the air with three conductors (see Figure 2) whose current flow is in the opposite direction to the real conductor. The magnitude of the current will be 200 A and the number of images is related to the angle between the iron boundary and the air $(270° - 90°)$.

Horizontal magnetic intensity components:

$$\frac{200}{2\pi}\left[\frac{1}{0.05} + \frac{1}{0.15} + \frac{0.15}{0.17^2} - \frac{0.05}{0.094^2}\right]$$

$$= \frac{200}{2\pi} \times 26.2 \text{ A/m}$$

Vertical magnetic intensity components:

$$-\frac{200}{2\pi}\left[\frac{0.08}{0.094^2} + \frac{0.08}{0.17^2}\right]$$

$$= -\frac{200}{2\pi} \times 11.82 \text{ A/m}$$

$$\text{Overall magnetic intensity at point P} = \frac{200}{2\pi} \sqrt{26.2^2 + 11.82^2}$$

$$= \frac{200}{2\pi} \times 28.75$$

$$\text{Flux density at point P} = \frac{4\pi}{10^7} \times 1000 \times \frac{200}{2\pi} \times 28.75 \text{ T}$$

$$= 1.15 \text{ T}$$

The direction is given by $-\tan^{-1} \dfrac{11.82}{26.2}$ or $\underline{-24.4°}$.

**Example 3.11**

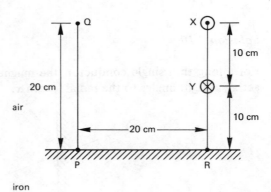

In the diagram X and Y represent long thin parallel conductors, perpendicular to the plane of the paper and parallel to the surface of an infinite iron plate of high permeability represented by PR.

The conductors each carry a steady current of 2000 A in the directions indicated. Calculate: (a) the magnetic field strength, $\overline{H}$, in magnitude and direction at the points P and Q, and (b) the mechanical force per unit length on conductor X.

(IEE Part 3)

*Solution 3.11*

Two image conductors X′ and Y′ must be set up to represent the effect of the iron on the two conductors situated in air, as shown in Figure 1. The image conductors X′ and Y′ carry current in the same direction as X and Y, respectively. The magnetising force $\overline{H}$ for each conductor, including the images, is shown in the diagram.

It should be clear that the tangential components cancel out, leaving

$$\overline{H}_N = 2 \times \frac{I}{2\pi r} \times \cos \alpha$$

where $r$ is the radial distance. For X and X′ at P,

$$\overline{H}_N = \frac{2 \times 2000 \times 20 \times 10^{-2}}{2 \times \pi \times 800 \times 10^{-4}} = 1592 \text{ A/m}$$

For Y and Y′ at P,

$$\overline{H}_N = \frac{2 \times 2000 \times 20 \times 10^{-2}}{2 \times \pi \times 500 \times 10^{-4}} = 2546 \text{ A/m}$$

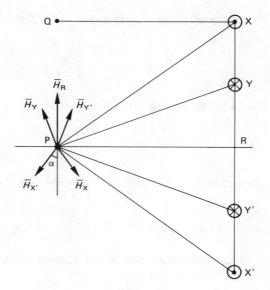

**Figure 1**

Overall magnetising force at P = 954 A/m acting *vertically upwards*.

To evaluate the magnetising force at point Q, consider Figure 2, which shows the field component due to each conductor together with its image.

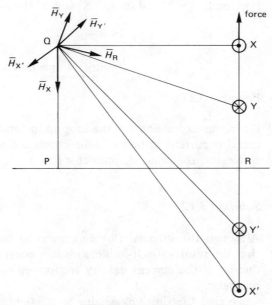

**Figure 2**

$$\bar{H}_X = \frac{2000 \times 10^3}{2\pi \times 20} = 1592 \text{ A/m}$$

$$\bar{H}_Y = \frac{2000 \times 10^2}{2\pi \times 22.36} = 1424 \text{ A/m}$$

$$\bar{H}_{X'} = \frac{2000 \times 10^2}{2\pi \times 44.72} = 712 \text{ A/m}$$

$$\bar{H}_{Y'} = \frac{2000 \times 10^2}{2\pi \times 36} = 884 \text{ A/m}$$

65

Total for vertical components $= -1592 + \dfrac{1424 \times 20}{22.36} - \dfrac{712 \times 20}{44.72} + \dfrac{884 \times 20}{36}$

$$= -1592 + 1274 - 318 + 491 \ \text{A/m}$$

$$= -145 \ \text{A/m}$$

Total for horizontal components $= 1424 \times \dfrac{10}{22.36} - 712 \times \dfrac{40}{44.72} + \dfrac{884 \times 30}{36} \ \text{A/m}$

$$= 637 - 637 + 737 \ \text{A/m}$$

$$= 737 \ \text{A/m}$$

Resultant magnetic intensity at point Q $= [145^2 + 737^2]^{\frac{1}{2}} \ \text{A/m}$

$$= \underline{751 \ \text{A/m}}$$

acting at an angle $\tan^{-1}$ (145/737) to the line QX – that is, $-11.1°$, as shown in Figure 2.

The mechanical force which acts on conductor X is due to the magnetic field in which X lies – that is,

$$\text{flux density} \times \text{current} \times \text{conductor length}$$

or

$$\dfrac{4\pi \times 2000^2 \times 10^2}{10^7 \times 2\pi \times 10} + \dfrac{4\pi \times 2000^2 \times 10^2}{10^7 \times 2\pi \times 30} - \dfrac{4\pi \times 2000^2 \times 10^2}{10^7 \times 2\pi \times 40}$$

For conductor Y and images X' and Y' the mechanical forces

$$= 8 + \dfrac{8}{3} - 2$$

$$= \underline{8.66 \ \text{N upwards per unit length}}$$

## Example 3.12

Derive an expression for the loop inductance for a pair of parallel overhead lines carrying current in opposite directions, a distance $D$ apart, in air, each with radius $r$. (Neglect the internal conductor flux.)

(IEE Part 3)

### Solution 3.12

Although the internal flux linkage is to be neglected, it should be remembered that the resultant self-inductance is a constant quantity $\mu_0/8\pi$ H/m for each conductor, if the current density is assumed to be uniform and the material is non-magnetic.

To find the flux linkage due to the field surrounding the conductors, apply the magnetic work law at point P.

The magnetising force $H$ at P is given by

$$\bar{H}_x \times 2\pi x = I$$

and

$$\bar{H}'_x \times 2\pi(D - x) = -I$$

Total magnetising force $= \dfrac{I}{2\pi x} + \dfrac{I}{2\pi(D - x)} \ \text{A/m}$

Total flux density at P $= \dfrac{\mu_0 I}{2\pi} \left[\dfrac{1}{x} + \dfrac{1}{D - x}\right] \text{T}$

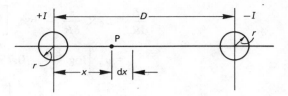

To evaluate the total flux linkage, consider a small radial strip width $dx$ around the conductor carrying $I$ A and of axial length 1 m, as shown in the diagram. Then

$$\text{flux linking this strip} = \frac{\mu_0 I}{2\pi} \left[ \frac{dx}{x} + \frac{dx}{D - x} \right]$$

Total flux linkage between the conductors per loop metre length is

$$\int_r^{D-r} \frac{\mu_0 I}{2\pi} \left[ \frac{dx}{x} + \frac{dx}{D - x} \right] = \frac{\mu_0 I}{\pi} \log_e \left[ \frac{D - r}{r} \right] \text{Wb-turns}$$

Self-inductance between the conductors

$$L = \frac{\mu_0}{\pi} \log_e \left[ \frac{D - r}{r} \right] \text{H per loop metre}$$

## Example 3.13

A wire of radius 10 mm is bent into a circle of mean radius 1000 mm and carries a sinusoidal current of which the r.m.s. value is 10 kA. The inductance of a circle of wire may be assumed to be given by

$$L = \mu_0 R \left[ \log_e \frac{8R}{r} - 1.75 \right] \text{H}$$

where $r$ is the radius of the wire, $R$ is the radius of the circle and $\mu_0$ is the permeability of free space. Calculate the peak and the average value of the tensile force in the wire.

## Solution 3.13

The electromagnetic force on a conductor of self-inductance $L$, carrying current $i$, is of the form

$$F = \tfrac{1}{2} i^2 \frac{dL}{dx} \text{ N}$$

Consider the diagram, with the small shaded element of the circular loop, at an angle $\theta$ to the diameter. The force will act radially on the loop; hence,

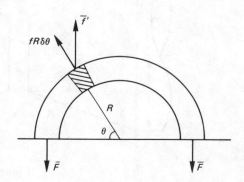

$$\frac{dL}{dR} = \mu_0 R \frac{r}{\delta R} \frac{8}{r} + \mu_0 \left[ \log_e \frac{8R}{r} - 1.75 \right]$$

$$= \mu_0 \left[ \log \frac{8R}{r} - 0.75 \right]$$

Radial force $= \frac{1}{2} i^2 \mu_0 \left[ \log_e \frac{8R}{r} - 0.75 \right]$

and the force per unit length of circumference is given by

$$f = \frac{1}{2} \frac{i^2 \mu_0}{2\pi R} \left[ \log_e \frac{8R}{r} - 0.75 \right]$$

Hence, the radial force on the shaded element in the diagram is $f \times R \times \delta\theta$, while the vertical component of this force is $f'$, where

$$f' = f \times R \times \delta\theta \times \sin\theta$$

Thus,

$$2F = \int_0^\pi fR \sin\theta \; d\theta$$

$$2F = 2fR$$

$$F = \frac{\mu_0 i^2}{4\pi} \left[ \log_e \frac{8R}{r} - 0.75 \right] \text{ N}$$

The peak value of current is $\sqrt{2} \times 10^4$ A; therefore,

$$F_{peak} = \frac{4\pi \times 2 \times 10^8}{10^7 \times 4\pi} \left[ \log_e \frac{8R}{r} - 0.75 \right] \text{ N}$$

$$= 118.7 \text{ N}$$

Average value $= \frac{1}{2} F_{peak} = \underline{59.35 \text{ N}}$

**Example 3.14**

An electromagnet has a soft adjustable air-gap of length $g$ between truncated conical soft iron poles, as shown in Figure 1. The flux can be taken as concen-

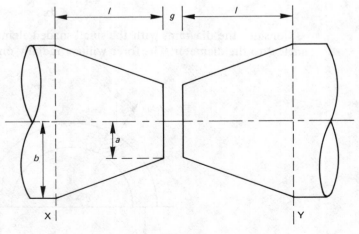

**Figure 1**

trated uniformly within the circular area of radius $a$. Assuming the iron to have a constant relative permeability $\mu_r$, estimate the m.m.f. required for that part of the magnetic circuit between planes X and Y for a gap of flux density $B$.

### Solution 3.14

The m.m.f. for the part XY of the magnet may not exceed 3500 AT. If $b/a = 3$, $l$ = 120 mm and the relative permeability of the iron is 240, find the maximum gap length $g$ for a gap flux density of 2.0 T.

From Figure 1 deduce Figure 2 giving a variable distance $x$ to obtain m.m.f. for XY. (m.m.f. = flux × circuit reluctance.)

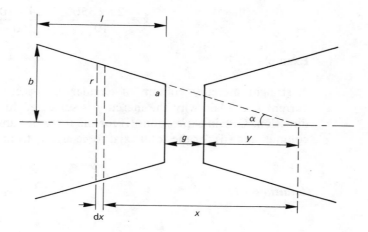

**Figure 2**

$$\text{Area } A_x = \pi r^2$$

$$\frac{r}{x} = \frac{b - a}{l}$$

Thus,

$$A_x = \pi \frac{(b - a)^2 \, x^2}{l^2}$$

$$\text{m.m.f. } (x) = \frac{\Phi \, dx \, l^2}{\mu \pi (b - a)^2 \, x^2}$$

$$\text{total m.m.f. for one pole piece} = \int_y^{y+l} \frac{\Phi \, l^2 \, dx}{\mu \pi (b - a)^2 \, x^2}$$

$$= \frac{\Phi \, l^2}{\mu \pi (b - a)^2} \left[ \frac{l}{y \, (y + l)} \right]$$

Now

$$y = \frac{a \, l}{b - a}$$

Therefore,

$$\text{m.m.f.} = \frac{\Phi \, l}{\pi \mu a b} \quad (\Phi = B \pi a^2)$$

$$\text{total m.m.f. for both poles} = \frac{2\,\Phi l}{\pi \mu ab} = \frac{2Bla}{\mu b}$$

$$\text{m.m.f. for the air-gap} = \frac{\Phi\,g}{\mu_0 \pi a^2} = \frac{Bg}{\mu_0}$$

$$\text{m.m.f.}_{XY} = \frac{2Bla}{\mu b} + \frac{Bg}{\mu_0} = \frac{B}{\mu_0}\left[\frac{2la}{\mu_r b} + g\right]$$

Thus,

$$3500 = \frac{2 \times 10^7}{4\pi}\left[\frac{2 \times 12 \times 10^{-2}}{240 \times 3} + g\right]$$

or

$$g = \frac{2\pi \times 3500}{10^7} - \frac{24 \times 10^{-2}}{240 \times 3} \text{ m} = \underline{1.87 \text{ mm}}$$

## Example 3.15

A straight mercury column of circular cross-section, radius $R$, carries a direct current $I$. Explain why the mercury is subjected to a radial force, and deduce its direction. Obtain expressions (i) for the force per unit area at a radius $r$ within the column, and (ii) for the total axial force arising from this effect.

(CEI Part 2)

*Solution 3.15*

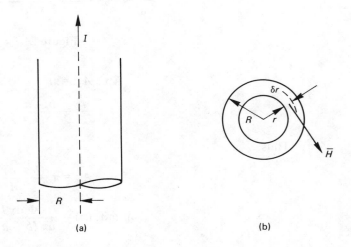

(a)  (b)

$$\text{Current density } \overline{J} = \frac{I}{\pi R^2} \text{ A/m}^2$$

at any radius $r$ — the enclosed current is

$$\overline{J} \times \pi r^2 = \frac{Ir^2}{R^2} \text{ A}$$

$$\text{Magnetic intensity } \overline{H}(r) \times 2\pi r = \frac{Ir^2}{R^2}$$

i.e.

$$\overline{H}(r) = \frac{Ir}{2\pi R^2} \text{ A/m}$$

70

In the annular ring, radius $r$, thickness $\delta r$, the current $= \delta I = 2\pi r \, \delta r \, \overline{J}$ — i.e.

$$\delta I = 2\pi r \delta r \, \frac{I}{\pi R^2} = \frac{2Ir\delta r}{R^2} \; \text{A}$$

This current shell *is* perpendicular to the magnetic intensity $\overline{H}(r)$; hence, force must exist, acting *inwards* in a radial direction.

Consider a unit length of mercury column, and let the pressure due to the incremental current shell be $\delta p(r)$. Then

$$\delta p(r) \cdot 2\pi r = \delta I \times \overline{B}(r) = \delta I \times \mu \times \overline{H}(r)$$

$$= \frac{\mu 2I \, r \, \delta r}{R^2} \times \frac{Ir}{2\pi R^2}$$

$$\delta p(r) = \frac{\mu I^2 \, r\delta r}{2\pi^2 \, R^4} \; \text{N/m}^2$$

Therefore, total inward pressure at the radius $r$ (due to current in liquid mercury outside this radius) is

$$p(r) = \int_r^R \frac{\mu I^2 \, r \mathrm{d}r}{2\pi^2 \, R^4} \; \text{N/m}^2 = \frac{\mu I^2 \, [R^2 - r^2]}{4\pi^2 \, R^4} \; \text{N/m}^2$$

But the liquid pressure acts in all directions. Therefore,

$$\text{axial force} = \int_0^R 2\pi r \, p(r) \, \mathrm{d}r$$

$$= \frac{\mu I^2}{2\pi R^4} \int_0^R (\mu R^2 - r^3) \, \mathrm{d}r$$

$$= \frac{\mu I^2}{2\pi R^4} \left[ \frac{R^4}{2} - \frac{R^4}{4} \right]$$

$$= \frac{\mu I^2}{8\pi} \; \text{N}$$

## 3.3 Unworked Problems

### Problem 3.1

A coaxial cable comprises a thin copper sheath of inner radius $a$ and a solid copper rod of radius $b$ separated by a perfect insulant.

Derive an expression for the total energy stored in the magnetic field per unit length of insulant and rod when the cable carries direct current.

Using this expression, show that there are radial pressures on the sheath and on the rod of amplitudes $P_a$ and $P_b$, respectively, where $P_a/P_b = b^2/a^2$. Show that $P_a$ and $P_b$ act in opposite directions.

(Engineering Council Part 2)

$$\left[ W = \frac{\mu I^2}{4\pi} \log_e \frac{b}{a} \; \text{J} \right]$$

**Problem 3.2**

A long concentric cable consists of a solid central cylindrical conductor of radius $a$ covered with insulation to a radius $b$ over which is a thick annular conductor of inner radius $b$ and outer radius $c$. The cable carries current in opposite directions in the two conductors, respectively, and the current density in each conductor is uniform. Obtain an expression for the magnetic field strength $\bar{H}$ at any radius: (i) inside the central conductor, (ii) in the insulation, (iii) in the outer conductor, (iv) outside the cable.

Sketch the variation of $\bar{H}$ with radius. Obtain an expression for the self-inductance of the cable, and calculate its value per metre length if $a = 0.5$ cm, $b = 1.0$ cm and $c = \sqrt{2}$ cm. The relative permeability of the conductors and insulation is unity.

(IEE Part 3)

[0.22 $\mu$ H/m]

**Problem 3.3**

Show that the magnetic field intensity $\bar{H}$ at a distance $x$ from an infinitely long straight conductor carrying a current $I$ is given by

$$\bar{H} = \frac{I}{2\pi x} \text{ A/m}$$

Two such conductors of negligibly small cross-section, set parallel at a distance $2d$ apart, carry equal currents in opposite directions. Show that the lines of magnetic field intensity form a system of circles.

(CEI Part 2)

**Problem 3.4**

Show that the vector potential due to a current element can be defined as the work done in bringing a parallel unit test element (that is, $Idl = 1$) from infinity to the point considered.

Two long parallel wires carry a low-frequency alternating current in opposite directions. Derive an expression for the vector potential at any point and use it to sketch an arrangement that will measure the difference of vector potential between any two points on opposite wires, without an e.m.f. being generated in the leads.

(CEI Part 2)

**Problem 3.5**

The three conductors A, B and C of a three-phase transmission line are equilaterally spaced 1 m apart with conductor B vertically above conductor C. The line carries a balanced load of 10 MVA at 33 kV line voltage. Calculate the mechanical force per metre length in magnitude and direction, produced magnetically on each of the three conductors at the instant of peak current in conductor A.
[0.011 N/m; 0.0055 N/m; 0.0055 N/m]

**Problem 3.6**

A large circular coil of $N$ concentrated turns and mean radius $R$, and a similar but small coil of $n$ turns and radius $r$, are set parallel, a distance $x$ apart, with their centres on a common axis perpendicular to the planes of the coils. Determine the mutual inductance between the coils.

Let the large coil carry a steady current $I$, and the small coil move towards it at a velocity $u$. Obtain an expression for the e.m.f. induced in the small coil, and show that it has a maximum value when $x = \frac{1}{2} R$.

(CEI Part 2)

$$\left[ \frac{\mu_0}{25\sqrt{5}} \frac{48\pi\, Nnr^2 u}{R^2} \text{ V} \right]$$

**Problem 3.7**

(a) State the vector equation giving the Biot–Savart law — that is, the magnetic flux density $B$ due to a current element $idl$. Using this expression or otherwise, find the magnitude of $\bar{B}$ at a distance $r$ from an infinitely long straight conductor carrying a current $i$.

(b) Two long straight parallel conductors, of small cross-section and spaced a distance $2d$, carry equal currents $i_m \cos(100\pi t)$ in opposite directions. A small circular search loop of radius $a$ is placed with its centre distant $r$ from the axis of symmetry, as shown in the diagram.

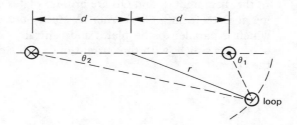

Assuming that $a \ll d$, and that $r \gg d$ (so justifying the approximation $\theta_1 = \theta_2$), determine the maximum e.m.f. that can be induced in the search loop, stating the position(s) and attitude(s) of the loop for this condition.

(CEI Part 2)

$$\left[ \text{e.m.f.}_{\text{max}} = \frac{\pi a^2\, \mu_0\, 100\, di_{\text{max}}}{r^2}; \text{small loop } \theta = 0 \text{ or } 180°; \text{plane is that containing} \right.$$

$$\left. \text{the conductors} \right]$$

**Problem 3.8**

In the diagram on p. 74 A and A′ are long parallel conductors which are also parallel to the surface of an infinite plate YOY′ of infinitely permeable iron. The conductors carry equal steady currents in opposite directions. Derive an expression for the normal component of magnetic flux density $\bar{B}$ at any point P on the surface of the plate. Find values of $y$ for which (a) $\bar{B}$ is zero, and (b) $\bar{B}$ is a maximum.

If $a = 40$ mm, $b = 60$ mm, and the current in each conductor is 100 A, calculate the normal component of flux density at the point c.

(IEE Part 3)

$$\left[ \frac{\mu_0 I}{\pi} \left[ \frac{(y-b)}{(y-b)^2 + a^2} - \frac{(y+b)}{(y+b)^2 + a^2} \right] \text{ T}; y_{\text{min}} = \pm (a^2 + b^2)^{\frac{1}{2}}; y_{\text{max}} = \right.$$

$$\left. \pm [a^2 + b^2 + 2a\,(a^2 + b^2)]^{\frac{1}{2}}; 0; 0.3 \text{ mT} \right]$$

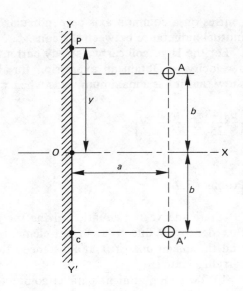

## Problem 3.9

In the diagram, OA and OB are infinite plates of high magnetic permeability meeting at O to form a 60° corner. A steady current $I$ flows in the long conductor C, which is parallel to the plates and centrally situated as shown. Sketch the system of images which, with the current in C, will closely represent the magnetic field of the current.

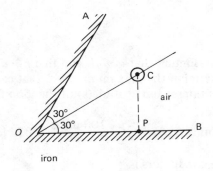

If OC = 200 mm and $I = 800$ A: (a) calculate the force per metre length on the conductor and show the direction of the force, (b) determine the magnitude and direction of the magnetic field strength at a point P just above the surface OB.
[1.6 N; 1312 A/m]

## Problem 3.10

An air-cored solenoid of length $2l$ is uniformly wound with fine wire. There are $n$ turns per unit length, the mean radius of the turns is $r$ and there is a steady current $i$ in the winding. Derive an expression for the magnetic field strength at any point along the axis of the solenoid.

The solenoid is to be used as the primary of a standard mutual inductor. The secondary consists of a short cylinder, wound with 50 turns of fine wire, placed coaxially and centrally inside the solenoid. If $n = 100$ turns per cm and the ratio $l/r = 2$, calculate the required mean radius of the secondary coil to give a mutual inductance $M = 1$ mH.

The secondary winding is now moved from the centre to one end of the primary solenoid. Estimate the new value of the mutual inductance.

$$\left[ \frac{ni}{2} (\cos \beta - \cos \alpha); H_C = \frac{nil}{(r^2 + l^2)^{\frac{1}{2}}}; H_{\text{end}} = \frac{nil}{(4l^2 + r^2)^{\frac{1}{2}}}; r = 23.7 \text{ mm}; \right.$$

$$\left. M = 0.55 \text{ mH} \right]$$

## Problem 3.11

A coaxial cable comprises an inner cylindrical conductor of radius $r$ within a tubular conductor of outer radius $R$, the two being separated by an annular insulating layer of negligible radial thickness. The conductors carry equal currents in opposite directions, and have the same current density. Show that the expression for the inductance per unit length of cable is independent of the radii $r$ and $R$.

(CEI Part 2)

$$\left[ L = \frac{\mu}{8\pi} \text{ H/m} \right]$$

## Problem 3.12

A coaxial cable consists of an outer conductor of soft copper tube with a mean radius of 10 mm and 1 mm thick. During a short-circuit the current rises to $2 \times 10^5$ A in a few microseconds. Given that the tensile strength of the copper is 2000 kg/cm$^2$, estimate whether the tube will burst.
[peak stress = 1300 kg/cm$^2$; no]

## Problem 3.13

Show that the total energy stored in the magnetic field of two coils with self-inductance $L_1$ and $L_2$, carrying currents $i_1$ and $i_2$, respectively, is

$$\tfrac{1}{2} i_1^2 L_1 + \tfrac{1}{2} i_2^2 L_2 \pm i_1 i_2 M$$

where $M$ is the mutual inductance between the coils.

Use this expression to deduce the relationship between the force of attraction or repulsion between the coils and the rate of change of mutual inductance with displacement between the coils. With the aid of this relationship describe briefly the action of an elementary rotary machine comprising a fixed and a moving coil.

(CEI Part 2)

## Problem 3.14

Two large iron plates, one in a horizontal plane and the other in a vertical plane, intersect to form a right-angled corner. A long, straight conductor of small, circular cross-section is mounted in the corner parallel with the plates, at a distance $a$ from the vertical plate and $b$ from the horizontal plate. If the conductor carries a steady current and the iron is of very high magnetic permeability, make a sketch to show the magnetic field distribution in the space round the conductor and between the plates.

Calculate the magnitude and direction of the force on the conductor per metre length if the conductor carries a current of 1 kA and if $a = 300$ mm and $b = 400$ mm.
[0.61 N]

**Problem 3.15**

A concentric cable consists of two thin-walled tubes, of mean radii $r$ and $R$, respectively. Derive an expression for the inductance of the cable per unit length. The cable carries a sinusoidal short-circuit current of 3 kA (r.m.s.). The mean radius of the outer tube is 20 mm and its radial thickness is 2 mm. Assuming uniform current density in the conductor, calculate the peak tensile stress in the material of the outer tube.
[1460 kg/m²]

**Problem 3.16**

If a constant-current circuit expands owing to the forces set up by its own current, show that the mechanical work done is equal to the increase in the magnetic energy stored in the inductance of the circuit.

A round-section wire, radius $r$ = 3 mm, is bent into a circle of radius $R$ = 300 mm, and carries a sinusoidal current of 5000 A. The inductance of the circuit is given by

$$L = \mu_0 \, R \left[ \log_e \frac{8R}{r} - 1.75 \right] \text{H}$$

Assuming that the radius of the wire remains constant for any small change in the radius of the circle, calculate the peak and average values of the tensile stress in the wire.
[$1.05 \times 10^6$ N/m² ; $0.52 \times 10^6$ N/m²]

**Problem 3.17**

A magnetic flux crosses the plane interface between two media of different permeabilities. Show that, on either side of the interface, the normal components of flux density $\overline{B}$ are the same and the tangential components of field strength $\overline{H}$ are the same.

A long straight conductor, in air, carrying a steady current $I$, lies parallel to the plane surface of an infinite iron block of relative permeability $\mu_r$. Show that the magnetic field strength $\overline{H}$ at any point (a) in the air is the same as that due to current $I$ in the conductor and an image conductor $I_1$ below the surface with the iron removed, where

$$I_1 = I \left[ \frac{\mu_r - 1}{\mu_r + 1} \right]$$

and (b) in the iron is the same as that due to current

$$I_2 = I \left[ \frac{2}{\mu_r + 1} \right]$$

in the conductor with the whole space filled with iron.

If the conductor is 100 mm above the block with $I$ = 1500 A and $\mu_r$ = 5.3, calculate the force per metre length on the conductor.

(IEE Part 3)

[1.536 N/m]

# 4 Electromagnetic Induction and Forces

## 4.1 Fact Sheet

This chapter is concerned with mechanical forces in magnetised systems and consequently with changes in magnetic field energy when mechanical movement occurs in the system.

### (a) Faraday's Law (Transformer Action)

When the magnetic flux linking an electrical circuit of $N$ turns is altered, an e.m.f. is induced in the circuit which is, at any instant of time, equal to the negative rate of change of flux linkage:

$$\text{e.m.f.} = -N \frac{d\Phi}{dt} \text{ V}$$

The minus sign is an indication that the e.m.f. is in such a direction as to produce a current whose flux, if added to the original flux, would reduce the magnitude of the e.m.f.

If the magnitude only of the e.m.f. is required without the instantaneous direction, the minus sign may be omitted and the e.m.f. is relative to the supply.

This statement that the induced voltage acts to produce an opposing flux is known as *Lenz's law*.

This equation can be applied to current-carrying conductors, but it can also be applied to any circuit path in space through which the flux may be changing.

It is also known that the electromotive force in any closed circuit anywhere is defined as the line integral of the electric field about this circuit:

$$\text{e.m.f.} = \oint \overline{E} \cdot dx$$

$$\oint \overline{E} \cdot dx = -N \frac{d\Phi}{dt}$$

Since

$$\Phi = \int_s \overline{B} \cdot ds$$

then

$$\oint \overline{E} \cdot dx = -\frac{\partial}{\partial t} \int_s \overline{B} \cdot ds$$

for a constant field and moving circuit, and

$$\oint \overline{E} \cdot \mathrm{d}x = - \int \frac{\partial \overline{B}}{\partial t} \cdot \mathrm{d}s$$

for a stationary circuit and changing field.

Now the e.m.f. around the closed path ($\oint \overline{E} \cdot \mathrm{d}x$) is of course the induced voltage. Also, $\int_s \overline{B} \cdot \mathrm{d}s$ gives the total flux through the surface $s$, bounded by the closed circuit moving with respect to the field. Or, if the circuit is stationary, this is the changing field which is linking with the circuit.

### (b) Stokes's Theorem

Stokes's theorem applied to electric fields states that the line integral of a vector function around a closed contour is equal to the *curl* of that vector function over any surface having the contour as its bounding edge:

$$\oint \overline{E} \cdot \mathrm{d}x = \int_s (\nabla \times \overline{E}) \cdot \mathrm{d}s$$

Hence,

$$\int_s (\nabla \times \overline{E}) \cdot \mathrm{d}s = - \int_s \frac{\partial \overline{B}}{\partial t} \cdot \mathrm{d}s$$

Then

$$\mathrm{curl}\, \overline{E} = - \frac{\mathrm{d}\overline{B}}{\mathrm{d}t} \quad \text{(Maxwell equation)}$$

The line integral of an electric field about a closed circuit need not be zero for a time-varying field, and so work can be done in taking a charge around a closed circuit in such a field. The energy involved comes from the changing magnetic field — it is distributed through the field, its density in a region in the field, with a flux density $\overline{B}$ T and a magnetising force $\overline{H}$ A/m, being given by $\frac{1}{2} \overline{B} \cdot \overline{H}$ J/m$^3$.

### (c) Mechanical Forces

It is usual to classify mechanical forces which originate from magnetic field movements under two headings.

#### (i) *Interaction*

Interaction occurs when an electric current directed at right angles to a magnetic field component experiences a force proportional to the product of current and flux density.

#### (ii) *Alignment*

Alignment occurs when ferromagnetic parts experience forces urging them towards a region in which the magnetic field is stronger, or tending to align them in such a way as to reduce the magnetic flux path (i.e. by rotation or translation).

Some systems will produce both forms of force, but it is often assumed that only the magnetic force is present.

### (d) Faraday's Law (Motor Action)

An alternative form to the transformer action is

$$\text{e.m.f.} = \oint (\overline{v} \times \overline{B}) \cdot dx$$

where $dx$ is a differential element of wire length. This is derived as follows. For a wire moving in a steady magnetic field, the force on an element of current circuit $i\, dx$ is

$$d\overline{F}_m = i\, dx \times \overline{B}$$

Thus,

$$\overline{F}_m = q(\overline{v} \times \overline{B})$$

But

$$\overline{F}_s = q\overline{E}$$

so

$$\overline{E} = \overline{v} \times \overline{B}$$

But

$$\text{e.m.f.} = \oint \overline{E} \cdot dx$$

Thus,

$$\text{e.m.f.} = \oint (\overline{v} \times \overline{B}) \cdot dx$$

This equation therefore holds for charges in a vacuum or moving through a wire circuit.

### (e) Energy Conversion

An electromechanical system with a magnetic field as the working medium has an energy input $W_e$ from the electric source, an input $W_m$ from the mechanical drive, and a total energy input $(W_e + W_m)$ which is balanced internally by a magnetic field energy $W_f$, an energy storage $W_s$ such as kinetic energy of motion or potential energy of deformation together with non-useful energy such as heat.

A distinction must be made between static forces and dynamic conditions. The former are evaluated on virtual work (energy principles), while the latter involve time-changing conditions.

#### (i) *Static Force*

In a singly excited system in which movement is linear in direction $x$, say, or rotational with angle $\theta$, the force or torque is derived from virtual work at constant current or an elemental displacement:

$$\overline{F} = \frac{dW_f}{dx}$$

or

$$\overline{T} = \frac{dW_f}{d\theta}$$

In a doubly excited system, one of the most useful forms in terms of the self-
and mutual inductance is

$$\overline{F} = \frac{dW_f}{dx} = \frac{1}{2} i_1^2 \frac{dL_1}{dx} + \frac{1}{2} i_2^2 \frac{dL_2}{dx} \pm i_1 i_2 \frac{dM}{dx}$$

### (ii) Dynamic Force

When a system is in motion, there are two causes of change in the flux linkage,
because for a constant voltage both current and self-inductance are variable. Then

$$v = N \frac{d\Phi}{dt} = N \frac{d(Li)}{dt}$$

$$= N \left[ L \frac{di}{dt} + i \frac{dL}{dt} \right]$$

$$= N \left[ L \frac{di}{dt} + i \frac{dL}{dx} \cdot \frac{dx}{dt} \right]$$

$\frac{dx}{dt} = u$ is the speed of movement. The mechanical power is $\frac{1}{2} u \left[ \frac{dL}{dx} \right] i^2$.

### (f) Displacement Current

Consider a voltage applied to a resistor and capacitor in parallel — then the nature
of the current flow through the resistor is different from that through the capacitor. Thus, a constant voltage across a resistor produces a continuous flow of
current of constant value, while the current through a capacitor will be constant
only while the voltage is changing.

Then the current $i_1$ through the resistor is given by

$$i_1 = \frac{V}{R}$$

and a current $i_2$ through the capacitor is given by

$$i_2 = \frac{dq}{dt} = C \frac{dV}{dt}$$

The instantaneous charge $q$ on the capacitor is given by $q = CV$.

The current $i_1$ is a conduction current, while the current $i_2$ through the capacitor is referred to as the *displacement current*. Although this current does not
actually flow through the capacitor, the external effect is as though it did, since as
much current flows out of one plate as flows into the opposite one.

This circuit idea may be extended to three dimensions by supposing that the
resistor and capacitor elements each occupy a volume — area $A$ and length $d$.

Thus, the electric field $\overline{E}$ equals the potential $V$ across the element, divided by
its length,

$$\overline{E} = \frac{V}{d} \quad \text{(a simple form)}$$

The current density $\overline{J}_1$ inside the resistor is given by

$$\overline{J}_1 = \overline{E} \times \sigma = \frac{i_1}{A}$$

where $\sigma$ is the conductivity of the medium inside the resistor element.

If the capacitor is considered as a parallel plate type, then

$$C = \frac{\epsilon \times A}{d}$$

where $A$ is the area of the plates and $d$ the spacing between them.

$$i_2 = \frac{\epsilon \times A \times d}{d} \times \frac{d\overline{E}}{dt} = \epsilon A \frac{d\overline{E}}{dt}$$

The current density $\overline{J}_2$ inside the capacitor equals the permittivity of the non-conducting medium filling the capacitor element, multiplied by the time rate of charge of the electric field, i.e.

$$\overline{J}_2 = \frac{i_2}{A} = \epsilon \frac{d\overline{E}}{dt}$$

Recalling that the electric flux density $\overline{D} = \epsilon\overline{E}$, then

$$\overline{J}_2 = \frac{d\overline{D}}{dt}$$

Hence, $\overline{J}_1$ is the conduction current density $\overline{J}_{cond}$, while $\overline{J}_2$ is a displacement current density $\overline{J}_{disp}$. Also, current density $\overline{J}$, electric flux density $\overline{D}$ and the electric field intensity $\overline{E}$ are actually space vectors, which all have the same direction in isotropic media; thus,

$$\overline{J}_{cond} = \sigma\overline{E}$$

and

$$\overline{J}_{disp} = \epsilon \frac{\partial\overline{E}}{\partial t} = \frac{\partial\overline{D}}{\partial t}$$

$$\overline{J}_{total} = \overline{J}_{cond} + \overline{J}_{disp}$$

According to Ampere's law, the line integral of $\overline{H}$ around a closed contour is equal to the current enclosed. Where both conduction and displacement currents are present, this current is the *total current*. Thus,

$$\oint \overline{H} \cdot dx = \int_s (\overline{J}_{cond} + \overline{J}_{disp}) \cdot ds$$

or

$$\oint \overline{H} \cdot dx = \int_s \left( \sigma\overline{E} + \epsilon \frac{\partial\overline{E}}{\partial t} \right) \cdot ds$$

The line integral of $\overline{H}$ on the left-hand side of this equation is around the boundary of the surface $s$ over which the surface integral is taken on the right-hand side of this equation.

This equation may also be written in the form

$$\oint \overline{H} \cdot dx = \int_s \left( \overline{J} + \frac{\partial\overline{D}}{\partial t} \right) \cdot ds$$

where $\overline{J}$ refers only to conduction current density.

Apply Stokes's theorem to the above equation:

$$\nabla \times \overline{H} = \overline{J} + \frac{\partial\overline{D}}{\partial t} \quad \text{(Maxwell's first equation)}$$

or

$$\nabla \times \bar{H} = \sigma\bar{E} + \epsilon\,\frac{\partial\bar{E}}{\partial t}$$

It should be noted that when the electric field varies harmonically with time ($\bar{E} = \bar{E}_0 \sin \omega t$), the conduction and displacement currents are in time phase quadrature — that is,

$$\bar{J} = \sigma\bar{E} = \sigma\bar{E}_0 \sin \omega t$$

and

$$\frac{\partial\bar{D}}{\partial t} = \epsilon\,\frac{\partial\bar{E}}{\partial t} = \omega\epsilon\bar{E}_0 \cos \omega t$$

Thus, when $\omega t = 0$, the displacement current is a maximum and the conduction current is zero. On the other hand, when $\omega t = \pi/2$, the conduction current is a maximum and the displacement current is zero.

Thus, the displacement current leads the conduction current by $90°$ — i.e.

$$\bar{E} = \bar{E}_0\, e^{j\omega t}$$

Then

$$i_{\text{disp}} = \frac{\epsilon\partial\bar{E}}{\partial t} = \epsilon j\omega\bar{E}_0\, e^{j\omega t} = j\omega\epsilon\bar{E}$$

Hence,

$$\nabla \times \bar{H} = \sigma\bar{E} + j\omega\epsilon\bar{E} = (\sigma + j\omega\epsilon)\,\bar{E}$$

The operator j in the displacement current term and its absence in the conduction current term signify that the displacement current is advanced in phase by $90°$ with respect to the conduction current.

## 4.2 Worked Examples

### Example 4.1

Consider the fixed rectangular loop of area $A$ shown in the diagram. The flux density $\bar{B}$ is normal to the plane of the loop and is uniform over the area of the loop. However, the magnitude of $B$ varies harmonically with respect to time, as given by $\bar{B} = B_0 \cos \omega t$. Find the total e.m.f. induced in the loop.

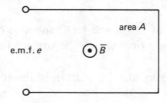

### Solution 4.1

This is a case of flux density $\bar{B}$ change only, since there is no motion. Hence, the total e.m.f. induced in the loop is

$$e = -\int_s \frac{\partial\bar{B}}{\partial t} \cdot \mathrm{d}s = \underline{A\omega B_0 \sin \omega t\ \text{V}}$$

The e.m.f. appears at the terminals of the loop. Since the velocity is zero, there can be no motional induction.

### Example 4.2

Consider the rectangular loop shown in the diagram. The width $d$ of the loop is constant, but its length $x$ is increased uniformly with time by moving the sliding conductor at a uniform velocity $v$. The flux density $\bar{B}$ is everywhere the same (normal to the plane of the loop) and is constant with respect to time. Find the total e.m.f. induced in the loop.

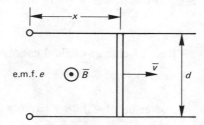

### Solution 4.2

This is a pure case of motion only, the flux density $\bar{B}$ being constant

$$\text{e.m.f.} = \oint (\bar{v} \times \bar{B}) \cdot \mathrm{d}x$$

$$= \bar{v} \times \bar{B} \times l \; \text{V}$$

The entire e.m.f. in this case is induced in the moving conductor of length $d$. Since $\partial \bar{B}/\partial t = 0$, the e.m.f. by transformer induction is zero, but if calculated from flux linkage theory, it is

$$\text{e.m.f.} = -\frac{\partial}{\partial t} \int_{s} \bar{B} \cdot \mathrm{d}s$$

$$= -\bar{B} \times d \times \frac{\mathrm{d}x}{\mathrm{d}t} = -\bar{B} \times d \times \bar{v} \; \text{V}$$

This is the same as the first answer, except for the sign, which is arbitrary in this question.

### Example 4.3

The coil of a d.c. relay has been energised and the armature is moving to *close* the air-gap. At a given instant the speed of the armature is found to be 0.223 m/s; the coil inductance is 2.2 H and is changing with armature position at 680 H/m. An ammeter in the coil circuit reads 0.28 A and is falling at 13 A/s.

Determine for this instant (i) the induced coil voltage, (ii) the power balance and (iii) the force exerted on the armature.

*Solution 4.3*

The armature is moving to reduce the gap $x$; therefore, the armature is moving in direction $-x$ where the speed of the armature is $u = -0.223$ m/s – i.e. decelerating. $u = \mathrm{d}x/\mathrm{d}t$.

(i)  Coil voltage $v = L\,\dfrac{\mathrm{d}i}{\mathrm{d}t} + i\,\dfrac{\mathrm{d}L}{\mathrm{d}t} = L\,\dfrac{\mathrm{d}i}{\mathrm{d}t} + i\,\dfrac{\mathrm{d}L}{\mathrm{d}x}\cdot\dfrac{\mathrm{d}x}{\mathrm{d}t}$

$\qquad\qquad\qquad = 2.2 \times (-13) + 0.28 \times (-680) \times -0.223$ V

$\qquad\qquad\qquad = -28.6 + 42.46$ V

$\qquad\qquad\qquad = \underline{13.86\text{ V}}$

(ii) Mechanical power $= \frac{1}{2} \times (-0.223) \times (-680) \times 0.28^2$ W

$\qquad\qquad\qquad\quad = \underline{6\text{ W}}$

$\qquad$ Rate of change of field energy $\dfrac{\mathrm{d}W_f}{\mathrm{d}x} = \frac{1}{2} \times 0.28^2 \times (-680)$ J/m

$\qquad\qquad\qquad\qquad\qquad\qquad\qquad = -26.66$ J/m

$\qquad$ Power input $= 0.28 \times 13.86 = \underline{3.9\text{ W}}$

(iii)  Mechanical force $= \dfrac{6}{-0.223} = -27$ N

**Example 4.4**

The diagram shows an actuator with a spring-loaded armature and equal-area pole faces. When the coil current is zero, the spring (of stiffness $k$) is unstrained and

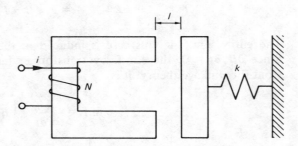

the air-gap length is $l_0$. Neglecting losses, iron-circuit reluctance and fringing and leakage fluxes, show that the electrical energy input to reduce the air-gap length from $l_0$ to $l_1$ is given by

$$W_e = \tfrac{1}{2}\,k\,(l_0^2 - l_1^2)$$

(CEI Part 2)

*Solution 4.4*

Let a change in the air-gap be a distance $x$ when the spring is unstrained. Hence, $l = (l_0 - x)$ or $x = (l_0 - l)$.

$$\text{Flux } \Phi = \frac{Ni}{\dfrac{2l}{A\mu_0}} = \frac{Ni\,A\mu_0}{2l}$$

where $A$ is the area of the pole face.

$$\text{Self-inductance } L = \frac{\Phi N}{i} = \frac{N^2 A \mu_0}{2(l_0 - x)}$$

Therefore,

$$\frac{\mathrm{d}L}{\mathrm{d}x} = -\frac{N^2 A \mu_0}{2(l_0 - x)^2} = -\frac{L}{(l_0 - x)}$$

At any instant during the movement of the armature, the electrical force is equal and opposite to the mechanical force:

$$\tfrac{1}{2} i^2 \frac{\mathrm{d}L}{\mathrm{d}x} = -kx$$

$$\tfrac{1}{2} i^2 \times \left(-\frac{L}{l_0 - x}\right) = -kx$$

$$\tfrac{1}{2} L i^2 = kx(l_0 - x) = \text{field energy}$$

At the end of the armature movement,

electrical energy input = work done against spring + change in field energy

$$W_{\text{elec}} = W_{\text{mech}} + W_{\text{field}}$$

$$W_{\text{mech}} = \int_0^{x_1 = l_0 - l_1} kx \, \mathrm{d}x = \tfrac{1}{2} k (l_0 - l_1)^2$$

Field energy at the start, when $x = 0$:

$$W_{\text{field1}} = k \times 0 \times (l_0 - 0) = 0$$

Field energy at the end, when $x = x_1 = l_0 - l_1$:

$$W_{\text{field2}} = k(l_0 - l_1)(l_0 - l_0 + l_1)$$

$$= k(l_0 - l_1) l_1$$

$$W_{\text{elec}} = \tfrac{1}{2} k(l_0 - l_1)^2 + k(l_0 - l_1) l_1 - 0$$

$$= \tfrac{1}{2} k l_0^2 - k l_1 l_0 + \tfrac{1}{2} k l_1^2 + k l_0 l_1 - k l_1^2$$

$$= \tfrac{1}{2} k l_0^2 - \tfrac{1}{2} k l_1^2$$

$$= \underline{\tfrac{1}{2} k (l_0^2 - l_1^2)}$$

### Example 4.5

Consider the loop and sliding conductor of Example 4.2. The flux density $\overline{B}$ is normal to the plane of the loop and is uniform everywhere. The sliding conductor moves with a uniform velocity $v$. The magnitude of the flux density is varying sinusoidally with time, and is given by

$$\overline{B} = B_0 \cos \omega t$$

Find the total e.m.f. induced in the loop.

(Leeds Polytechnic)

*Solution 4.5*

This example is simple but involves both motion and a time-varying magnetic field.

The e.m.f. $e_m$ due to the motion is given by

$$e_m = \oint (\bar{v} \times \bar{B})\, dx = \bar{v}\bar{B}\, d$$

$$= \bar{v}\, dB_0 \cos \omega t$$

The e.m.f. $e_t$ due to the time-varying field is

$$e_t = \int \frac{\partial \bar{B}}{\partial t}\, ds = \omega x dB_0 \sin \omega t$$

Thus,

$$\text{total e.m.f.} = e_t + e_m$$

$$= v dB_0 \cos \omega t + \omega x dB_0 \sin \omega t$$

$$= \underline{B_0\, d[v^2 + (\omega x)^2]^{\frac{1}{2}} \sin (\omega t + \phi)}$$

where $\phi = \tan^{-1} (v/\omega x)$ and $x$ is the instantaneous loop length. [Use the trigonometric identity of $\sin (A + B)$.]

## Example 4.6

A three-phase transmission line carrying balanced three-phase currents consists of three equilaterally spaced, parallel conductors. Show that at a point equidistant from all three conductors there is a pure rotating magnetic field and find an expression for the field strength and its velocity of angular rotation. Determine the value of the magnetic field strength when the spacing between conductors is 1 m and the line is carrying 10 MVA at 33 kV line voltage.

(IEE Part 3)

## Solution 4.6

It is already known that a current-carrying conductor creates a magnetic field of strength $\bar{H} = I/2\pi d$ A/m for a long conductor. In this problem the distance $d$ is the same for each conductor (see part (a) of diagram), but since it is a balanced three-phase system of conductors, there is a time phase difference between the currents:

$$i_R = I_m \cos \omega t$$

$$i_Y = I_m \cos \left( \omega t - \frac{2\pi}{3} \right)$$

$$i_B = I_m \cos \left( \omega t + \frac{2\pi}{3} \right)$$

Therefore, the corresponding magnetic field strength moduli are

$$|h_R| = H_m \cos \omega t$$

$$|h_Y| = H_m \cos \left( \omega t - \frac{2\pi}{3} \right)$$

$$|h_B| = H_m \cos \left( \omega t + \frac{2\pi}{3} \right)$$

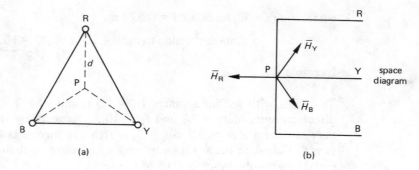

(a)                                                                  (b)

at the point P, 120° spacing and perpendicular to the distance $d$ from each conductor (see part (b) of diagram). Alternatively, expressing the yellow and blue phase magnetic field in terms of red phase:

$$h_Y = |h_R| e^{-j120°}$$

and

$$h_B = |h_R| e^{+j120°}$$

j is a 90° space rotation operator. Thus, the resultant magnetic intensity at the point P is

$$H_m \cos \omega t + H_m \cos\left(\omega t - \frac{2\pi}{3}\right) e^{-j(2\pi/3)} + H_m \cos\left(\omega t + \frac{2\pi}{3}\right) e^{+j(2\pi/3)}$$

or

$$H_m \left[ \cos \omega t + \cos \frac{2\pi}{3} \cos\left(\omega t - \frac{2\pi}{3}\right) + \cos \frac{2\pi}{3} \cos\left(\omega t + \frac{2\pi}{3}\right) \right.$$
$$\left. - j \left[ \sin \frac{2\pi}{3} \cos\left(\omega t - \frac{2\pi}{3}\right) - \sin \frac{2\pi}{3} \cos\left(\omega t + \frac{2\pi}{3}\right) \right] \right]$$

$$= H_m \left[ \cos \omega t + 2 \cos^2 \frac{2\pi}{3} \cos \omega t - j\, 2 \sin^2 \frac{2\pi}{3} \sin \omega t \right]$$

$$= H_m [1.5 \cos \omega t - j\, 1.5 \sin \omega t]$$

$$= \underline{1.5 \, |H_m| \, e^{-j\omega t} \text{ with clockwise rotation}}$$

[The rotating flux direction may be reversed by interchanging any two connections of the three-phase system.]

The above expression shows that a rotating field is produced at a point equidistant from the three conductors which is constant at $1.5 \, |H_m|$ A/m and has an angular frequency of $\omega$ rad/s.

For the numerical part of the question,

$$\sqrt{3} \times V_L \times I_L = 10 \times 10^6$$

$$I_L = \frac{10^7}{\sqrt{3} \times 33 \times 10^3} \text{ A} = 175 \text{ A}$$

Peak current value $= \sqrt{2} \times 175 = 247.5$ A

$$\text{Magnetic field strength} = \frac{247.5}{2\pi \times 0.577} \text{ A/m}$$

$$= 68.27 \text{ A/m}$$

where $d = (\sin 30/\sin 60) \times 1 = 0.577$ m.

Constant field strength $= 1.5 \times 68.27 = \underline{102.4 \text{ A/m}}$

**Example 4.7**

Two coils with self-inductances $L_1 = 1.5$ H and $L_2 = 0.03 + 0.005 \cos 2\theta$ H carry direct currents of $I_1 = 7$A and $I_2 = 40$ A, respectively. If the mutual inductance between them is $M = 0.2 \cos \theta$ H, sketch the torque as a function of rotor position $\theta$. Calculate the maximum torque and show that the contribution from the variable self-inductance is 1/15 of the total.

*Solution 4.7*

For the geometry of the machine, one must decide whether $L_1$ or $L_2$ is the rotor — Figure 1 shows $L_2$ as the rotating coil.

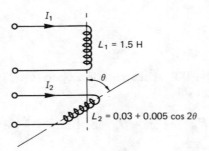

**Figure 1**

Use the known torque equation between stator and rotor windings:

$$T = \tfrac{1}{2} i_1^2 \frac{dL_1}{d\theta} + \tfrac{1}{2} i_2^2 \frac{dL_2}{d\theta} + i_1 i_2 \frac{dM}{d\theta}$$

$$= \tfrac{1}{2} \times 7^2 \frac{d}{d\theta} (1.5) + \tfrac{1}{2} \times 40^2 \times \frac{d}{d\theta} (0.03 + 0.005 \cos 2\theta)$$

$$+ 7 \times 40 \times \frac{d}{d\theta} (0.2 \cos \theta)$$

$$= 0 + 800 (-0.01 \sin 2\theta) + 280 (-0.2 \sin \theta)$$

$$T = - [8 \sin 2\theta + 56 \sin \theta]$$

$$\frac{dT}{d\theta} = - [16 \cos 2\theta + 56 \cos \theta]$$

For maximum torque $\qquad 16 \cos 2\theta + 56 \cos \theta = 0$

or $\qquad\qquad\qquad\qquad \cos 2\theta + 3.5 \cos \theta = 0$

Thus, $\qquad\qquad\qquad (2 \cos^2 \theta - 1) + 3.5 \cos \theta = 0$

$$\cos^2 \theta + 1.75 \cos \theta - 0.5 = 0$$

$$\cos \theta = \frac{-1.75 \pm \sqrt{(1.75^2 + 2)}}{2}$$

$$= \frac{-1.75 \pm 2.25}{2}$$

Thus, $\qquad\qquad\qquad\qquad\qquad\qquad \cos \theta = 0.25; \theta = 75.5°$

Therefore, $\qquad T_{max} = 8 \sin 151° + 56 \sin 75.5° = 3.88 + 54.22$

$$= \underline{58.1 \text{ Nm}}$$

The contribution from the variable self-inductance is

$$\underline{\frac{3.88}{58.1} = \frac{1}{15}}$$

(Torque sketch, Figure 2.)

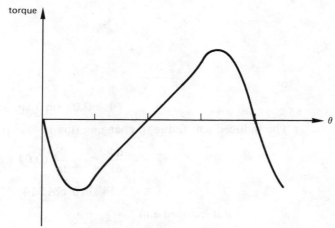

**Figure 2**

### Example 4.8

A single-turn square coil of 0.1 m side is placed in a uniformly distributed time-varying magnetic flux of density $\overline{B} = 1.0 \sin (100 \pi t)$ T. It is rotated about an axis through the centres of a pair of opposite sides, the axis being normal to the direction of the field, at a angular speed of 3000 rev/min. Assuming that the plane of the coil is parallel to the field direction at $t = 0$, evaluate the e.m.f. induced in the coil.

(CEI Part 2)

*Solution 4.8*

$$\text{Rotational speed} = \frac{3000}{60} = 50 \text{ rev/s}$$

$$\text{Linear velocity} = \pi \times 0.1 \times 50 = 15.7 \text{ m/s}$$

$$\text{Vertical velocity component } v_v = 15.7 \cos \theta$$

$$\text{Area of coil} = 0.1 \times 0.1 = 0.01 \text{ m}^2$$

$$\text{Induced e.m.f. due to flux cutting } e_g = -2\overline{B}lv_v$$

or

$$e_g = -2 \times 0.1 \times 1.0 \sin 314t \times 15.7 \cos \theta$$

$$= -3.14 \cos \theta \sin 314t$$

$$\text{Flux through the coil} = \Phi = \overline{B}A \sin \theta$$

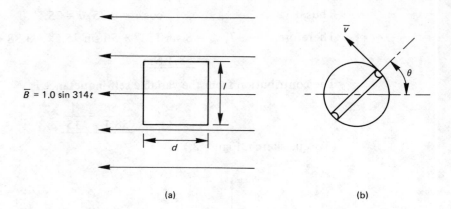

(a)                              (b)

or

$$\Phi = 0.01 \sin \theta \sin 314t$$

The induced e.m.f. due to changing flux is

$$e_c = -\frac{d\Phi}{dt} = -\frac{d}{dt}(0.01 \sin \theta \sin 314t)$$

$$= -3.14 \sin \theta \cos 314t \ \text{V}$$

total induced e.m.f. $= e_g + e_c$

$$= -3.14 \cos \theta \sin 314t - 314 \sin \theta \cos 314t$$

$$= \underline{-3.14 \sin(314t + \theta)}$$

Note that because the minus sign is used for $e_c$, it was also used for $e_g$. On the other hand, there is no basic reason why the direction taken cannot be considered as positive for $e_g$ so long as a positive sign is also taken for $e_c$, but the author feels that the first approach is more fundamental, since it could take into account the cases where the plane of the coil is *not* parallel at $t = 0$.

**Example 4.9**

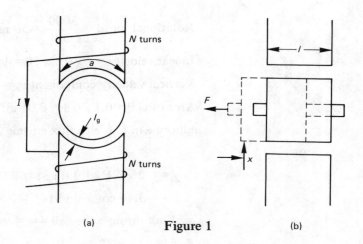

(a)              **Figure 1**              (b)

Figure 1 shows an elementary electrical machine in which flux fringing may be neglected, the iron parts may be assumed to have infinite permeability, and the gap length $l_g$ is short. Show that, when the rotor is displaced *axially* from the symmetrical position, an axial force of

$$\frac{\bar{B}^2 \times a \times l_g}{\mu_0}$$

where $\bar{B}$ is the flux density under the pole shoes, tends to restore the rotor to the position of symmetry. Sketch the relationship of the axial force to the displacement and add the curve that would be expected in practice.

(CEI Part 2)

### Solution 4.9

Side view Figure 1(b): consider a force $F$ giving a displacement $x$ of the rotor. Because the question states that flux fringing may be neglected and that the air-gap length is short, the solution can be simplified, using the basic law of magnetic circuitry:

$$\text{flux} = \frac{\text{m.m.f.}}{\text{reluctance}}$$

For an axial displacement $x$, the resultant flux is given by

$$\Phi = \bar{B} \times a \times (l - x) \ \text{Wb}$$

Then

$$\text{gap reluctance } S = \frac{2\,l_g}{a \times (l - x) \times \mu_0}$$

$$\text{magnetomotive force} = 2IN$$

$$= \bar{B} \times a \times (l - x) \times \frac{2\,l_g}{a\,(l - x)\,\mu_0}$$

or

$$2IN = \frac{2\bar{B}l_g}{\mu_0}$$

$$\text{Corresponding self-inductance } L = \frac{\Phi \times 2N}{I}$$

Therefore,

$$L = \frac{\bar{B} \times a \times (l - x) \times 2N}{I} \ \text{H}$$

$$\text{Axial force } F = \tfrac{1}{2}\, i^2\, \frac{\mathrm{d}L}{\mathrm{d}x}$$

$$= \tfrac{1}{2} \times I^2 \times \frac{\mathrm{d}}{\mathrm{d}x}\ \frac{\bar{B} \times a \times (l - x) \times 2N}{I} \ \text{N}$$

$$= \tfrac{1}{2} \times 2IN \times \bar{B} \times a \ \text{N}$$

$$= -\tfrac{1}{2} \times \frac{2\bar{B}l_g}{\mu_0} \times \bar{B} \times a \ \text{N}$$

$$= -\ \frac{\bar{B}^2 \times a \times l_g}{\mu_0} \ \text{N}$$

An alternative approach is to use the energy relation:

$$\text{potential energy} = \tfrac{1}{2} \times \frac{\overline{B}^2}{\mu_0} \times V \ \text{J}$$

$$\text{potential } V = 2 \times a \times l_g \times (l - x)$$

Therefore,

$$\text{energy} = \frac{\overline{B}^2}{\mu_0} \times a \times l_g \times (l - x)$$

For $0 < x < l$,

$$\text{axial force } F = \frac{\partial W}{\partial x}$$

$$= -\frac{\overline{B}^2 \times a \times l_g}{\mu_0}$$

The negative sign indicates that the force is in the opposite direction to that shown in Figure 1 — that is, the position of symmetry is attained.

The force–displacement sketch is shown in Figure 2.

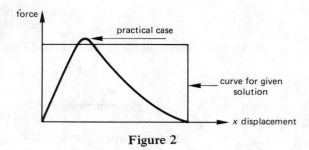

**Figure 2**

## Example 4.10

An elementary electrical machine, as shown in the diagram, has a distributed type of single-phase stator winding which produces a radial air-gap flux density $b = B_m \cos \theta \sin \omega t$. The rotor, of axial length $L$ and diameter $D$, carries two ten-turn full-pitch coils AA and BB, the planes of which are at 60°. The coils are connected in series and rotated at $\omega_r$ rad/s.

Derive an expression for the total e.m.f. generated in the coils at the instant when the plane of coil AA makes an angle of $\theta = \alpha$ with the maximum flux density plane.

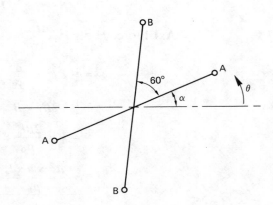

Using the derived expression, calculate the e.m.f. for the following values: supply frequency = 50 Hz, $t$ = 1 ms, $\alpha$ = 20°, $L$ = 100 mm, $\omega_r$ = 150 rad/s and $\bar{B}$ = 2 T.

**Solution 4.10**

Two types of e.m.f. are generated: (1) $e_R$ equals the rotational e.m.f. due to the conductors cutting the flux and (2) $e_t$ equals the transformer action e.m.f. due to alternating flux in the coils.

(1) For coil AA $\qquad b = B_{max} \cos \alpha \sin \omega t$

For coil BB $\qquad b = B_{max} \cos (\alpha + 60°) \sin \omega t$

The tangential velocity is $\qquad v = \omega_r \dfrac{D}{2}$ m/s

The number of cutting conductors per coil = 2 × 10, so that

$$e_R = - 2 \times 10 \times b \times L \times v \ \ \text{V}$$

$$= - 20L \ \omega_r \ \frac{D}{2} \ B_m \ [\cos \alpha \sin \omega t + \cos (\alpha + 60°) \sin \omega t]$$

$$= - 20L \ \omega_r \ \frac{D}{2} \ B_{max} \sin \omega t \ [1.5 \cos \alpha - 0.866 \sin \alpha]$$

$$= -10LD \ \omega_r \ B_{max} \sin \omega t \ [1.5 \cos \alpha - 0.866 \sin \alpha]$$

(2) The flux through coil AA is

$$\Phi_A = \int_{-(\pi - \alpha)}^{+\alpha} \frac{D}{2} \times L \times B_{max} \times \sin \omega t \times \cos \theta \ d\theta$$

$$= + DLB_{max} \sin \omega t \sin \alpha$$

while the flux through coil BB is

$$\Phi_B = + DLB_{max} \sin \omega t \sin (\alpha + 60°)$$

Therefore,

$$e_t = - \frac{d\Phi}{dt} = - \frac{d}{dt} \ (10\Phi_A + 10\Phi_B)$$

$$e_t = - 10 \ DLB_{max} \ \omega \sin \alpha \cos \omega t - DLB_m \ \omega \sin (\alpha + 60°) \cos \omega t$$

$$= - 10 \ DLB_{max} \ \omega \cos \omega t \ [\sin \alpha + \sin (\alpha + 60°)]$$

$$= - 10 \ DLB_{max} \ \omega \cos \omega t \ [1.5 \sin \alpha + 0.866 \cos \alpha]$$

Hence, the total e.m.f., $e$, generated is given by $e_R + e_t$ V — that is,

$$e = - 10 \ LD\omega_r \ B_{max} \sin \omega t \ [1.5 \cos \alpha - 0.866 \sin \alpha]$$

$$\underline{= - 10 \ DLB_{max} \ \omega \cos \omega t \ [1.5 \sin \alpha + 0.866 \cos \alpha] \ \text{V}}$$

For the numerical part,

$$\omega t \equiv 2\pi \times 50 \times \frac{1}{10^3} \ \text{rad} = 0.314 \ \text{rad} = 18°$$

Therefore, $\sin \omega t$ = 0.309 and $\cos \omega t$ = 0.951. As $\alpha$ = 20°, $\sin \alpha$ = 0.342 and $\cos \alpha$ = 0.94; therefore,

$$e = -10 \times \frac{10}{10^2} \times \frac{5}{10^2} \times 150 \times 2 \times 0.309 \, [1.5 \times 0.94 - 0.866 \times 0.342] \text{ V}$$

$$= -10 \times \frac{10}{10^2} \times \frac{5}{10^2} \times 2 \times 2 \times \pi \times 50 \times 0.951 \, [1.5 \times 0.342 + 0.866 \times 0.94] \text{ V}$$

$$= -4.635 \, [1.41 - 0.296] - 29.88 \, [0.513 + 0.814] \text{ V}$$

$$= -5.16 - 39.65 \text{ V}$$

$$= -44.81 \text{ V}$$

### Example 4.11

A 1 m square single-turn loop carrying a current $i$ lies in the $(x, y)$ plane with its sides on the lines $x = \pm 0.5$ m and $y = \pm 0.5$ m. A small five-turn search coil of effective area 0.05 m² is placed in the $(x, y)$ plane at the origin. (a) Calculate the e.m.f. induced in the search coil if $i = 20 \sin 1000 \, t$. (b) Calculate the r.m.s. value of the search coil e.m.f. if $i = 20 \sin 1000 \, t + 5 \sin 3000 \, t$.

(CEI Part 2)

### Solution 4.11

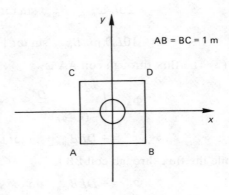

From the diagram, the magnetic field intensity at the centre of the loop ABCD is given by

$$\bar{H} = \frac{4 \times i}{\sqrt{2} \times \pi} \text{ AT}$$

Thus,

$$\text{flux density } \bar{B} = \frac{\mu_0 \times 4 \times i}{\sqrt{2} \times \pi} \text{ T}$$

so that the flux $\Phi$ linking the search coil is given by

$$\Phi = \frac{\mu_0 \times 4 \times i}{\sqrt{2} \times \pi} \times 0.05 \text{ Wb}$$

$$\text{Induced e.m.f. } e = -N \frac{d\Phi}{dt} \text{ V}$$

$$= -5 \frac{d\Phi}{dt} \text{ V}$$

(a) $\quad \Phi = \dfrac{4\pi}{10^7} \times \dfrac{4}{\sqrt{2}} \times \dfrac{0.05}{\pi} \; 20 \sin 1000\, t$

$\dfrac{\mathrm{d}\Phi}{\mathrm{d}t} = \dfrac{16}{\sqrt{2}} \times \dfrac{\cos 1000\, t}{10^4}$

Therefore,

$$e = -\dfrac{5 \times 16}{\sqrt{2} \times 10^4} \cos 1000\, t = \underline{-5.66 \cos 1000\, t \; \text{mV}}$$

(b) $\quad \Phi = \dfrac{4\pi}{10^7} \times \dfrac{4}{\sqrt{2}} \times \dfrac{0.05}{\pi} \times [20 \sin 1000\, t + 5 \sin 3000\, t]$

$\dfrac{\mathrm{d}\Phi}{\mathrm{d}t} = \dfrac{0.566}{10^7} [2 \times 10^4 \cos 1000\, t + 1.5 \times 10^4 \cos 3000\, t] \; \text{mV}$

$\qquad = -\,[5.66 \cos 1000\, t + 4.25 \cos 3000\, t] \; \text{mV}$

Therefore,

$$e_{\text{r.m.s.}} = \left[ \dfrac{5.66^2 + 4.25^2}{2} \right]^{\frac{1}{2}} \text{mV}$$

$$= \underline{5 \; \text{mV}}$$

## Example 4.12

A rotor is turned at angular speed $\omega_r$ rad/s, so that the inductance of the exciting windings of the electromagnetic device shown in the diagram varies sinusoidally between a maximum of $2L$ and a minimum of zero. A current $i = I_m \cos \omega t$ is maintained in the winding. Show that a sustained non-zero mean torque can be developed only if $\omega_r = \omega$.

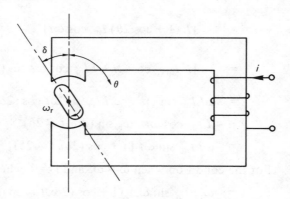

Derive an expression for this torque in terms of the position angle $\delta$ of the rotor axis at the instant of an exciting current zero. Derive also an expression for the voltage across the terminals of the exciting winding, the resistance of which is negligible.

*Solution 4.12*

$$\text{Inductance} = L\,[1 + \cos 2\theta]$$

$$\text{Torque } T = \tfrac{1}{2} \times i^2 \times \dfrac{\mathrm{d}L}{\mathrm{d}\theta}$$

$$= \tfrac{1}{2} \times i^2 \times [-2L \sin 2\theta]$$

$$T_{\text{inst}} = -I_m^2 \times \cos^2 \omega t \times L \times \sin 2\theta$$

$$= -L \times I_m^2 \times \sin 2\theta \left[ \frac{1 + \cos 2 \omega t}{2} \right]$$

$$= -\frac{L \times I_m^2}{2} \left[ \sin 2\theta + \sin 2\theta \cos 2 \omega t \right]$$

$$= -\frac{L \times I_m^2}{2} \left[ \sin 2\theta + \tfrac{1}{2} \sin (2 \omega t + 2\theta) + \tfrac{1}{2} \sin (2\theta - 2 \omega t) \right]$$

Now $\theta = \omega_r t - \delta$ or $\omega_r = d\theta/dt$; also $I = \sqrt{2} \times I_m$. Therefore,

$$T_{\text{inst}} = -L \times I^2 \left[ \sin (2\omega_r t - 2\delta) + \tfrac{1}{2} \sin (2\omega_r t - 2\delta + 2\omega t) \right.$$
$$\left. + \tfrac{1}{2} \sin (2\omega_r t - 2\delta - 2\omega t) \right]$$

The average value of each of these sine functions is zero *except* when $\omega_r = \omega$, because then $\tfrac{1}{2} \sin (2\omega_r t - 2\delta - 2\omega t)$ becomes $-\tfrac{1}{2} \sin 2\delta$, when, for a given torque and with $\delta$ constant,

$$T_{\text{average}} = \int_0^{2\pi/\omega} \frac{\tfrac{1}{2} LI^2 \sin 2\delta \; dt}{2\pi/\omega}$$

$$= \left[ \frac{\tfrac{1}{2} \times L \times I^2 \times \sin 2\delta \times t}{2\pi/\omega} \right]_0^{2\pi/\omega}$$

$$= \tfrac{1}{2} \times L \times I^2 \times \sin 2\delta$$

because with d.c. torque the average value is equal to the instantaneous value.

The voltage across the winding terminals is given by

$$v = \frac{d}{dt} (Li)$$

$$= \frac{d}{dt} \left[ L (1 + \cos 2\theta) I_m \cos \omega t \right]$$

$$= \frac{d}{dt} \left[ L I_{\text{max}} \cos \omega t + LI_m \cos \omega t \cos (2\omega_r t - 2\delta) \right]$$

$$= -\omega LI_m \sin \omega t - \omega LI_m \sin \omega t \cos (2\omega_r t - 2\delta)$$
$$- LI_m \cos \omega t \; 2\omega_r \sin (2\omega_r t - 2\delta)$$

$$= -\omega LI_m \sin \omega t \left[ 1 + \cos (2\omega_r t - 2\delta) \right] - LI_m \; 2\omega_r \cos \omega t \sin (2\omega_r t - 2\delta)$$

For the condition when $\omega = \omega_r$ and $i \neq 0$, when $\theta = 0$,

$$v = -\omega_r LI_m \sin \omega_r t \left[ 1 + \cos (2\omega_r t - 2\delta) \right] - 2\omega_r LI_m \cos \omega_r t \sin (2\omega_r t - 2\delta)$$

As $\theta = \omega_r t - \delta$ and $\delta$ is constant, this voltage expression can be expressed as

$$v = -\omega_r LI_m \sin \omega_r t (1 + \cos 2\delta) - 2\omega_r LI_m \cos \omega_r t \sin 2\theta$$

## Example 4.13

Find the displacement current density in a conductor through which a conduction current of 1 A is flowing. The frequency is 60 Hz and the conductor is made of copper with a conductivity of $58 \times 10^6$ S/m, while the relative permeability and permittivity are both unity. The diameter of the wire is 1 mm.

*Solution 4.13*

$$\nabla \times \bar{H} = \bar{J}_c + \frac{\partial \bar{D}}{\partial t}$$

Assume that the electric intensity $\bar{E} = \bar{E}_0 \cos \omega t$; then

$$\bar{J}_c = \sigma \bar{E} = \sigma \bar{E}_0 \cos \omega t$$

$$\frac{\partial \bar{D}}{\partial t} = \frac{\mathrm{d}}{\mathrm{d}t} (\epsilon_0 \bar{E}) = - \epsilon_0 \omega \bar{E}_0 \sin \omega t$$

The ratio between displacement current and conduction current is

$$\left| \frac{\frac{\partial \bar{D}}{\partial t}}{\bar{J}_c} \right| = \frac{\omega \epsilon_0}{\sigma} = \frac{2 \times \pi \times 60 \times 1}{58 \times 10^6 \times 36\pi \times 10^9}$$

$$= 5.75 \times 10^{-17}$$

As $I_c = 1$ A, $\qquad\qquad I_D = 5.75 \times 10^{-17}$ A

For a wire of diameter 1 mm, the cross-sectional area is $0.785 \times 10^{-6}$ m² and the conduction current density is given by

$$\bar{J}_c = \frac{1}{0.785 \times 10^{-6}} = 1.27 \times 10^6 \text{ A/m}^2$$

from which

$$\left| \frac{\partial \bar{D}}{\partial t} \right| = 5.75 \times 10^{-17} \times 1.27 \times 10^6 \text{ A/m}^2$$

$$= \underline{73 \times 10^{-12} \text{ A/m}^2}$$

# 4.3   Unworked Problems

**Problem 4.1**

A torque motor comprises cylindrical stator and rotor members; each carries a two-pole single-phase winding. The respective winding inductances are 3.0 and 0.9 H, and when the stator and rotor windings are coaxial, their mutual inductance is 1.8 H. Resistances are negligible. Stating any simplifying assumptions, develop an expression for the mean torque on the rotor; evaluate this for a stator current of 7.07 A, with the rotor winding short-circuited and an angle of 30° between the winding axes.

(CEI Part 2)

[77.88 Nm]

**Problem 4.2**

A copper disc of 150 mm diameter is located at the centre of a long solenoid of length 1 m, having a diameter of 160 mm. The solenoid is wound with 1200 turns. The disc is arranged to rotate about an axis coincident with the axis of the solenoid at 1800 rev/min. Brush take-offs are provided at the centre and at the edge of the disc. If the current in the solenoid is 2 A, what is the e.m.f. between the brushes?

(Leeds Polytechnic)

[1.6 mV]

**Problem 4.3**

Comment on the difference implied in the following alternative statements of the Faraday law of electromagnetic induction:
(a) the e.m.f. is equal to the rate of change of flux turns;
(b) the e.m.f. is equal to the turns times the rate of change of flux.

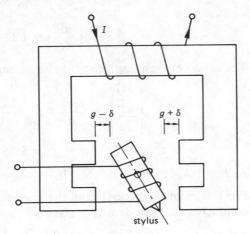

The diagram shows an electromagnetic transducer with a soft iron armature pivoted between the poles of an electromagnet excited by a direct current $I$ in a coil of $N$ turns. In the symmetrical position, each of the four working air-gaps has an effective length $g$; vibratory motion of the stylus produces a *small* displacement $\delta$ of the armature, and an e.m.f. $e$ is consequently induced in the $n$-turn pickup coil. Prove that at any instant

$$e = \left[ \frac{\mu_0 nNIA}{g^2} \right] \left[ \frac{\mathrm{d}\delta}{\mathrm{d}t} \right]$$

where $A$ is the effective cross-sectional area of each gap. The reluctances of the iron paths are negligible.

(CEI Part 2)

**Problem 4.4**

Explain the generalised machine theory approach to the prediction of performance of a practical electrical machine. Derive, in terms of the usual quantities, the torque relationship for an electrical machine having one stator winding and one rotor winding.

The self-inductance of the stator and rotor windings of an electrical machine are 1.6 H and $(0.03 + 0.005 \cos \theta)$ H, respectively, and the mutual inductance between them is $(0.2 \cos \theta)$ H. The angle $\theta$ measures the axis position of the rotor winding with respect to the axis position of the stator winding. Calculate the maximum torque of the machine when the stator current is 8 A and the rotor current is 40 A.

$$\left[ T = \tfrac{1}{2} i_1^2 \frac{\mathrm{d}L_1}{\mathrm{d}\theta} + \tfrac{1}{2} i_2^2 \frac{\mathrm{d}L_2}{\mathrm{d}\theta} + i_1 i_2 \frac{\mathrm{d}M}{\mathrm{d}\theta} ; 68 \text{ Nm} \right]$$

**Problem 4.5**

The inductance of a single-phase two-pole reluctance motor is given by $L = (0.05 + 0.03 \cos 2\theta)$ H, where $\theta$ is the rotor position angle. When the motor is running at synchronous speed from a 50 V, 50 Hz, sinusoidal voltage supply, its load angle for a certain load is 45° and its power factor is 0.5 lagging. Derive an expression for the instantaneous torque of the motor, using the basic relationship

$$T_{inst} = \tfrac{1}{2} i^2 \frac{dL}{d\theta}$$

Using the derived expression, calculate $T_{inst}$ when the voltage has reached its maximum value.
[−0.114 Nm]

### Problem 4.6

A two-pole machine has a salient pole rotor, with an exciting winding carrying a direct current $I$ rotating within a cylindrical stator at an angular speed $\omega_r$ rad/s. A single-phase winding on the stator carries an alternating current $i = I_m \sin \omega t$. The self-inductance of the rotor winding is $L_{11}$, and of the stator is $L_{22} = L_0 - L_2 \sin 2\theta$, where $\theta$ is the angular position of the rotor m.m.f. axis relative to that of the stator winding. The mutual inductance between stator and rotor windings is $L_{12} \cos \theta$.

Explaining the physical meaning of the parameters and of the steps in the analysis, develop an expression for the torque. Show that the torque averages zero except when $\omega_r = \omega$, and determine its value for this condition.

(CEI Part 2)

$[\tfrac{1}{4} L_2 I_m^2 \cos 2\delta - \tfrac{1}{2} L_{12} I I_m \cos \delta ; \theta = (\omega_r t - \delta)]$

### Problem 4.7

The diagram shows an elementary electrical machine in which the ferromagnetic parts have infinite permeability. A winding (not shown) on the inner surface of

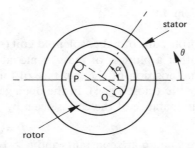

the stator established a radial gap flux density $B(\theta, t) = B_m \cos \theta \cos \omega t$. The rotor, of effective axial length $l$ and diameter $D$, carries a single-turn coil PQ. Obtain an expression for the e.m.f. induced in the coil when the rotor is driven at a speed $\omega_r$ rad/s and the position of coil side P is at angle $\theta = \alpha$ when $t = 0$.

What does the expression become (a) if $\omega_r = \omega$, (b) if $\omega_r = 0$ and the coil is fixed with coil side P at $\theta = \alpha$?

(CEI Part 2)

$[e = lD\omega_r B_m \cos \alpha; (a) lD\omega B_m \cos (\omega t - \alpha), (b) lD\omega B_m \sin \alpha \sin \omega t]$

### Problem 4.8

Show that the force $f$ tending to increase the air-gap length $x$ in a linear, singly excited electromechanical device with self-inductance $L$ and exciting current $i$ is given by

$$f = \tfrac{1}{2} i^2 (dL/dx)$$

99

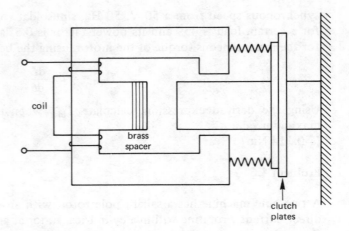

The diagram shows an electromagnetic clutch system. Two springs, each of stiffness 30 N/mm, press the plates together with a total force of 1000 N. The pole face of the actuator magnet has an area of 25 cm² and is capped by a brass shim 3 mm thick. The coil, which is supplied from a constant current source, has 500 turns and the clutch travel is 4 mm. Determine

  (i) the minimum coil current that just separates the clutch plates.

  (ii) the maximum coil current that, with 4 mm separation, just allows the plates to close.

Neglect iron reluctance, fringing and leakage fluxes.

Explain why the clutch cannot be held partly open.

(CEI Part 2)

[(i) 11.17 A; (ii) 5.33 A]

## Problem 4.9

The iron core of a d.c. solenoid coil (see diagram) comprises two parts: one fixed, the other a plunger of mass $m$ movable under the restraint of a spring of stiffness $K$. The position of the gap face of the plunger can vary between $x = 0$ (open gap) and $x = c$ (closed gap). In the open gap position the spring imposes zero restraint. The inductance of the coil is given by

$$L = a\,(1 + e^{bx})$$

where $a$ and $b$ are constants and $b > 1/c$.

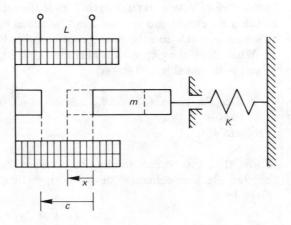

(a) Find an expression for the maximum coil current and the corresponding displacement $x$ for which the plunger is at rest in stable equilibrium with the gap partly closed.

(b) A constant current $I$, greater than that in (a), is maintained in the coil. The plunger is suddenly released from the open position $x = 0$. Find (i) the velocity with which the plunger hits the fixed core, and (ii) the energy supplied by or delivered to the source during the motion, neglecting coil resistance.

(CEI Part 2)

$$\left[ \text{(a) } I_m = \left[ \frac{0.735\ K}{ab^2} \right]^{\frac{1}{2}}, x = \frac{1}{b}\ ; \text{(b) (i)} \left[ \frac{aI^2\ (e^{bc} - 1) - Kc^2}{m} \right]^{\frac{1}{2}} ; \text{(ii) } aI^2\ (e^{bc} - 1) \right]$$

## Problem 4.10

A long straight non-magnetic cylindrical conductor of resistivity $\rho$ and radius $r$ lies in a uniform magnetic field that alternates sinusoidally at a low angular frequency $\omega$ and has an r.m.s. value of flux density $\overline{B}$. Derive expressions for the power loss per unit length of the conductor when its axis lies (i) in the direction of $\overline{B}$, (ii) at right angles to $\overline{B}$.

[Note $\int \sin^2 \theta \cos^2 \theta\ d\theta = \frac{1}{8} (\theta - \frac{1}{4} \sin 4\theta).$]

(CEI Part 2)

$$\left[ \text{(i) } \frac{\pi \omega^2 B^2\ r^4}{8\rho}\ ; \quad \text{(ii) } \frac{\pi \omega^2 B^2\ r^4}{4\rho} \right]$$

## Problem 4.11

Compute the peak value of the displacement current densities for the following: (i) a laser beam of frequency $10^5$ Hz and electric intensity $\overline{E} = 30$ kV/m, (ii) a field in a high-voltage cable of relative permittivity 4, electric field intensity $\overline{E} = 400 \sin 100\ \pi\ t$ kV/m and (iii) a radio wave of frequency 1 MHz and intensity 1 $\mu$V/m.

[(i) $1.67 \times 10^9$ A/m$^2$ ; (ii) 4.44 mA/m$^2$ ; (iii) 55.6 pA/m$^2$ ]

## Problem 4.12

For a coaxial cable of radii $a$, $b$ and a length $L$, with a permittivity $\epsilon$, evaluate the displacement current $I_D$ across an intermediate surface ($a < \rho < b$) with a sinusoidal applied voltage $V_m \sin \omega t$. Show that $I_D$ is independent of $\rho$ and equal to the charging current.

A 1500 m long cable has $a = 10$ mm, $b = 20$ mm, with $\epsilon_r = 3.6$. A voltage $\sqrt{2} \times 10^5 \sin 100\ \pi t$ is applied at one end with the far end on open circuit. Compute the magnetic field strength $H$ midway in the insulation, at the input end and halfway along the cable.

[204 A/m; 102 A/m]

## Problem 4.13

A long circular bar of non-ferrous metal is heated by a surrounding long concentric coil. The supply frequency is sufficiently high for induced currents in the bar to be considered confined to a thin surface layer and for the effects of curvature to be ignored. Determine expressions for

(i) the magnetic field strength within the bar at a radial distance $h$ from the bar surface,

(ii) the current density within the bar,

(iii) the impedance presented to the supply per unit length of the heating coil.

Use $H_0$ — magnetic field strength at bar surface
 $\delta$ — penetration depth
 $a$ — outer radius of bar
 $b$ — effective radius of heating coil
 $N$ — turns per unit axial length of heating coil

(Engineering Council Part 2A)

$$\left[\text{(i) } \frac{Ni\,b}{a+h}\;;\;\text{(ii) } \delta H_0 e^{-\delta h}\;;\;\text{(iii) } \mu_0 N^2 b 2\pi(b-a)\right]$$

## Problem 4.14

A rectangular rotating loop lies in a sinusoidally varying magnetic field $\overline{B} = B_0 \sin \omega t$ as shown in the diagram. The loop rotates with a uniform angular velocity $\omega_r$ rad/s. If the radius of the loop is $R$ and its length is $l$, find the total e.m.f. induced.

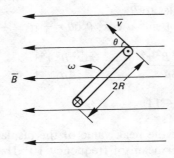

$$[2l\omega_r R B_m \cos\theta \sin\omega t + 2\omega l R \sin\theta\, B_m \cos\omega t]$$

# 5 Electromagnetic Waves

## 5.1 Fact Sheet

### (a) Maxwell's Equations

A number of relations developed in the preceding sections are brought together and considered as a group. These relations are known as Maxwell's equations. They relate the the main field parameters and consist of four expressions.

*Ampere's work law* relating the line integral $\overline{H}$ around a closed path to the current $I$ enclosed is given as

$$\oint \overline{H} \cdot \mathrm{d}x = I$$

Replacing the current by the surface integral of the conduction current density $\overline{J}_{\mathrm{cond}}$ over an area bounded by the path of integration of $\overline{H}$, then

$$\oint \overline{H} \cdot \mathrm{d}x = \int_{s} \overline{J}_{\mathrm{cond}} \cdot \mathrm{d}s$$

In more general terms, the displacement current density needs to be included; hence,

$$\oint \overline{H} \cdot \mathrm{d}x = \int_{s} \left( \overline{J}_{\mathrm{cond}} + \frac{\partial \overline{D}}{\partial t} \right) \cdot \mathrm{d}s$$

This is Maxwell's first equation in integral form. If Stokes's theorem is applied to this expression, then the differential form of Maxwell's first equation is obtained:

$$\nabla \times \overline{H} = \overline{J} + \frac{\partial \overline{D}}{\partial t}$$

The second of Maxwell's equations is obtained from *Faraday's law* relating the e.m.f. induced in a circuit to the time rate of decrease of the total magnetic flux linking the circuit:

$$e = -\frac{\mathrm{d}\Phi}{\mathrm{d}t}$$

Replacing the flux linkage $\Phi$ by the surface integral of $\overline{B}$ over the area bounded by the circuit,

$$e = -\frac{\mathrm{d}}{\mathrm{d}t} \int_{s} \overline{B} \cdot \mathrm{d}s$$

and replacing $e$ by the line integral of $\overline{E}$ around the circuit yields

$$\oint \overline{E} \cdot \mathrm{d}x = -\int_{s} \frac{\partial \overline{B}}{\partial t} \cdot \mathrm{d}s$$

The corresponding differential form is

$$\nabla \times \bar{E} = - \frac{\partial \bar{B}}{\partial t}$$

From the earlier work, Gauss' law relating the surface integral of the electric flux density $\bar{D}$ to the charge $q$ enclosed is given as

$$\int_s \bar{D} \cdot ds = q$$

Replacing $q$ by the volume integral of the charge density $\rho$ throughout the volume enclosed by the surface $s$, this last expression may be written as

$$\int_s \bar{D} \cdot ds = \oint_v \rho \, dv$$

This field relation is a generalisation of Gauss' law and is called Maxwell's electric field or third equation. It appears in integral form and applies to a finite volume $v$. Applying this equation to an infinitesimal volume, the corresponding differential relation is

$$\nabla \cdot \bar{D} = \rho$$

In the case of magnetic fields, the surface integral of $\bar{B}$ over a closed surface $s$ yields zero. Thus, the magnetic counterpart of Gauss' electric field relation is

$$\int_s \bar{B} \cdot ds = 0$$

with the corresponding differential form

$$\nabla \cdot \bar{B} = 0$$

The magnetic flux which issues from any closed surface is always zero. Other fundamental relations which are of importance when dealing with electromagnetic problems are

$$\nabla \cdot \bar{J} = - \frac{\partial \rho}{\partial t} \quad \text{(charge continuity)}$$

and the force relations

$$\bar{F}_s = q \times \bar{E}$$

and

$$\bar{F}_m = q \times \bar{v} \times \bar{B}$$

so that the field vectors $\bar{E}$ and $\bar{B}$ can be expressed in the form

$$\bar{F} = q \, (\bar{E} + v \times \bar{B})$$

The following relationships are usually obtained experimentally: $\bar{D} = \epsilon \bar{E}$, $\bar{B} = \mu \bar{H}$, and $\bar{J} = \sigma \bar{E}$, where $\epsilon$, $\mu$ and $\sigma$ are the permittivity, permeability and conductivity of the medium with which the problem may be concerned.

*For conductors and dielectrics*, the ratio $\sigma/\omega\epsilon$ is that between the conduction current density and the displacement current density; it can be used as the criterion for conductors and dielectrics ($\omega$ rad/s is the sinusoidal angular frequency). For good conductors, $\sigma/\omega\epsilon \gg 1$ at 30 000 MHz; for example, for copper the value is $3.5 \times 10^8$. For good dielectrics, $\sigma/\omega\epsilon \ll 1$; for example, for mica the value is $2 \times 10^{-4}$.

## (b) Maxwell's Equations in Free Space

This is a special case, where the current density $\bar{J}$ and the charge density $\rho$ are zero; thus the equations reduce to a simpler form.

In integral form the equations are

$$\oint \bar{H} \cdot dx = \int_s \frac{\partial \bar{D}}{\partial t} \cdot ds$$

$$\oint \bar{E} \cdot dx = - \int_s \frac{\partial \bar{B}}{\partial t} \cdot ds$$

$$\oint_s \bar{D} \cdot ds = 0$$

$$\oint_s \bar{B} \cdot ds = 0$$

while in differential form the equations are

$$\nabla \times \bar{H} = \frac{\partial \bar{D}}{\partial t}$$

$$\nabla \times \bar{E} = - \frac{\partial \bar{B}}{\partial t}$$

$$\nabla \cdot \bar{D} = 0$$

$$\nabla \cdot \bar{B} = 0$$

## (c) Maxwell's Equations for Harmonically Varying Fields

If it is assumed that the fields vary harmonically with time, Maxwell's equations may be expressed in another special form. Thus, if $\bar{D}$ varies with time, as given by

$$\bar{D} = D_0\, e^{j\omega t}$$

then

$$\frac{\partial \bar{D}}{\partial t} = j\omega D_0\, e^{j\omega t} = j\omega \bar{D}$$

Making the same assumption for $\bar{B}$, Maxwell's equations in integral form reduce to

$$\oint \bar{H} \cdot dx = (\sigma + j\omega\epsilon) \int_s \bar{E} \cdot ds$$

$$\oint \bar{E} \cdot dx = - j\omega\mu \int_s \bar{H} \cdot dx$$

$$\oint \bar{D} \cdot ds = \int_s \rho \, dv$$

$$\oint \bar{B} \cdot ds = 0$$

In differential form, the equations are

$$\nabla \times \overline{H} = (\sigma + j\omega\epsilon)\,\overline{E}$$

$$\nabla \times \overline{E} = -j\omega\mu\overline{H}$$

$$\nabla \cdot \overline{D} = \rho$$

$$\nabla \cdot \overline{B} = 0$$

### (d) Poynting's Vector

Poynting's vector is concerned with the magnitude and direction of the density of power flow in an electromagnetic field.

From Maxwell's first equation in differential form,

$$\nabla \times \overline{H} = \overline{J} + \frac{\partial}{\partial t}\,\overline{D}$$

$$\overline{E} \cdot \nabla \times \overline{H} = \overline{E} \cdot \overline{J} + \epsilon\overline{E}\,\frac{\partial}{\partial t}\,\overline{E}$$

Using the identity

$$\nabla \cdot (\overline{E} \times \overline{H}) = \overline{H} \cdot \nabla \times \overline{E} - \overline{E} \cdot \nabla \times \overline{H}$$

$$-\nabla \cdot (\overline{E} \times \overline{H}) + \overline{H} \cdot \nabla \times \overline{E} = \overline{J} \cdot \overline{E} + \epsilon\overline{E} \cdot \frac{\partial}{\partial t}\,\overline{E}$$

or

$$-\nabla \cdot (\overline{E} \times \overline{H}) = \overline{J} \cdot \overline{E} + \epsilon\overline{E} \cdot \frac{\partial}{\partial t}\,\overline{E} - \overline{H} \cdot \nabla \times \overline{E}$$

Hence,

$$-\nabla \cdot (\overline{E} \times \overline{H}) = \overline{J} \cdot \overline{E} + \tfrac{1}{2}\,\epsilon\,\frac{\partial}{\partial t}\,\overline{E}^2 - \overline{H}\left(\frac{-\partial}{\partial t}\,\overline{B}\right)$$

$$= \overline{J} \cdot \overline{E} + \tfrac{1}{2}\,\epsilon\,\frac{\partial}{\partial t}\,\overline{E}^2 + \tfrac{1}{2}\,\mu\,\frac{\partial}{\partial t}\,\overline{H}^2$$

Now integrate all the terms through a small volume d$v$, yielding

$$\int_{\text{vol}} -\nabla \cdot (\overline{E} \times \overline{H})\,\mathrm{d}v = \int_{\text{vol}} \overline{J} \cdot \overline{E}\,\mathrm{d}v + \int_{\text{vol}} \tfrac{1}{2}\,\epsilon\,\frac{\partial}{\partial t}\,\overline{E}^2\,\mathrm{d}v + \int_{\text{vol}} \tfrac{1}{2}\,\mu\,\frac{\partial}{\partial t}\,\overline{H}^2\,\mathrm{d}v$$

Use the divergence theorem on the term on the left-hand side to change the volume integral to a surface integral:

$$\int_{s} -(\overline{E} \times \overline{H}) \cdot \mathrm{d}s = \int_{\text{vol}} \overline{J} \cdot \overline{E}\,\mathrm{d}v \quad + \frac{\partial}{\partial t} \int_{\text{vol}} (\tfrac{1}{2}\,\epsilon\overline{E}^2 + \tfrac{1}{2}\,\mu\overline{H}^2)\,\mathrm{d}v$$

total instantaneous = instantaneous ohmic + rate of increase in electric
power into volume    loss in volume      and magnetic stored energy
                                               in the volume

Hence,

$$\text{total instantaneous power out of volume} = \oint_{s} (\overline{E} \times \overline{H}) \cdot \mathrm{d}s$$

$$\text{instantaneous power density } \overline{P} = \overline{E} \times \overline{H} \ \text{W/m}^2 \text{ of surface}$$

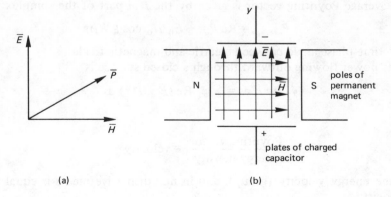

(a)

(b)

**Fig. 5.1**

This is Poynting's theorem, the vector $\overline{P}$ being known as Poynting's vector, sometimes referred to as a surface power density. Figure 5.1(a) defines the direction of the vector and agrees with the uniform plane wave for $\overline{H}_x$ and $\overline{E}_y$ with wave travel in the $z$ direction.

It should be remembered that in some situations $\overline{E} \times \overline{H}$ does not represent energy flow, as, for example, in Figure 5.1(b), a static magnetic field superimposed on a static electric field.

The integral of the normal component of $\overline{E} \times \overline{H}$ over a closed surface always gives the total power through the surface:

$$\int_s \overline{P} \cdot \mathrm{d}s = \text{power } p \text{ W}$$

where $p$ is power flowing out of a closed surface $s$. The Poynting vector $\overline{P}$ in the above relation is the instantaneous power density, and $p$ is the instantaneous power in watts.

When $\overline{E}$ and $\overline{H}$ change with time, it is important to know the average power:

$$\frac{1}{T} \int_0^T \overline{P} \, \mathrm{d}t$$

However, it is also readily obtained using complex notation:

$$\overline{P} = \tfrac{1}{2} \overline{E} \times \overline{H}^*$$

where

$$\overline{E} = E_0 \, e^{j\omega t}$$

$$\overline{H}^* = H_0 \, e^{-j(\omega t - \xi)}$$

$$\xi = \text{phase angle between } \overline{E} \text{ and } \overline{H}^*$$

$\overline{H}^*$ is the complex conjugate of $\overline{H}$, where

$$\overline{H} = H_0 \, e^{+j(\omega t - \xi)}$$

Quantity $\overline{H}$ and its complex conjugate $\overline{H}^*$ have the same space direction and the same amplitude $H_0$ but differ in sign in their phase relation.

If it is assumed that the space directions of $\overline{E}$ and $\overline{H}$ (or $\overline{H}^*$) are normal to each other, the complex Poynting vector is normal to the plane containing $\overline{E}$ and $\overline{H}^*$, and is

$$\overline{P} = \tfrac{1}{2} E_0 \, H_0 \, e^{j\xi}$$

Now the average Poynting vector is given by the real part of the complex vector

$$\overline{P}_{\text{average}} = \operatorname{Re} P = \tfrac{1}{2}\, E_0\, H_0\, \cos \xi \ \text{W/m}^2$$

where $\xi$ = time-phase angle between electric and magnetic fields.

Average power flowing outward through a closed surface is

$$\oint_s \operatorname{Re} P \ \mathrm{d}s = \tfrac{1}{2}\, \oint_s \operatorname{Re} (\overline{E} \times \overline{H}{}^*)\ \mathrm{d}s$$

and

$$\frac{\text{Poynting vector}}{\text{energy density}} = \text{velocity}$$

That is the energy velocity (group), and in non-dispersive media is equal to the phase velocity:

$$V_{\text{energy}} = \frac{\overline{E} \times \overline{H}}{\epsilon \overline{E}{}^2} = \frac{1}{\sqrt{\mu\epsilon}} = \text{velocity} \not> 3 \times 10^8 \ \text{m/s}$$

## 5.2  Worked Examples

### Example 5.1

A metal rod, of radius $r$, resistivity $\rho$ and relative permeability $\mu_r$, is arranged co-axially within a long magnetising coil of $N$ turns per unit length carrying an r.m.s. current $I$ of angular frequency $\omega$. Show that the magnetic field strength $\overline{H}$ at radius $x$ within the rod is given by

$$\frac{\partial^2 \overline{H}}{\partial x^2} + \frac{1}{x}\,\frac{\partial \overline{H}}{\partial x} + n^2\,\overline{H} = 0$$

where

$$n^2 = -\,\frac{\mathrm{j}\omega\mu_r\mu_0}{\rho}$$

Estimate the power dissipation per metre length in a rod of radius 50 mm within a coil of 40 turns per metre carrying 20 A at 250 kHz. The rod has a resistivity of 0.05 $\Omega$m and a relative permeability of 1.0. Ignore end effects, and assume that the currents in the rod do not appreciably affect the magnetic field strength due to the exciting current.

(CEI Part 2)

*Solution 5.1*

At radius $x$ within the rod (see diagram) let the field quantities induced by the exciting coil be $\overline{H}_x, \overline{E}_x$ and $\overline{J}_x$. [$\overline{H}_x$ in the axial direction, since it is a cylindrical

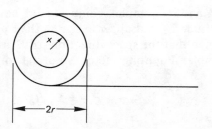

rod.] Due to the time-varying field $\overline{H}_x$, there will be an induced electric field $\overline{E}_x$, which, since there is no physical movement in the system, is given by

$$\overline{E}_x \times 2\pi x = - \int_s \frac{\partial \overline{B}}{\partial t} \cdot ds = - j\omega \int_0^x \overline{B}_a \times 2\pi a \, da$$

where $a$ is a dummy variable representing the radius.

$$\overline{J}_x = \sigma \overline{E}_x$$

Thus,

$$\overline{J}_x = - \frac{j\omega\sigma}{x} \int_0^x \overline{B}_a \times a \times da$$

or

$$x\overline{J}_x = - j\omega\sigma \int_0^x \overline{B}_a \times a \times da$$

Differentiate with respect to $x$:

$$x \frac{\partial \overline{J}_x}{\partial x} + \overline{J}_x = -j\omega\sigma x \overline{B}_x = -j\omega\mu\sigma x \overline{H}_x$$

But

$$\overline{J} = \text{curl } H$$

that is,

$$\overline{J}_x = - \frac{\partial \overline{H}_x}{\partial x}$$

Then

$$x \frac{\partial^2 \overline{H}_x}{\partial x^2} + \frac{\partial \overline{H}_x}{\partial x} - j\omega\mu\sigma x \overline{H}_x = 0$$

or

$$\frac{\partial^2 \overline{H}_x}{\partial x^2} + \frac{1}{x} \frac{\partial \overline{H}_x}{\partial x} + n^2 \overline{H}_x = 0$$

where

$$n^2 = -j\omega\mu\sigma = - \frac{j\omega\mu}{\rho}$$

[Reminder: $\sigma = 1/\rho$.]

Now $\oint \overline{H} \, dl = $ enclosed current $= \Sigma NI = \overline{H} \times 1$, as $\overline{H}$ is essentially constant and the $N$ turns are given per unit length.

$$\overline{E}_x = - \frac{j\omega\mu\overline{H}}{x} \int_0^x a \, da = - \frac{j\omega\mu\overline{H}x}{2}$$

As $\overline{J}_x = \sigma\overline{E}_x$, power density $= |\overline{J}_x\overline{E}_x| = \sigma \, |\overline{E}_x{}^2 |$

$$p_x = \frac{\sigma\omega^2\mu^2 N^2 I^2 x^2}{4}$$

$$\text{power dissipated per metre length} = \int_0^r 2\pi x p_x \, dx$$

$$= \frac{\pi \sigma \omega^2 \mu^2 N^2 I^2}{2} \int_0^r x^3 \, p_x \, dx$$

$$= \frac{\pi \sigma \omega^2 \mu^2 N^2 I^2}{8} r^4$$

$\omega = 2\pi f.$

$$\text{Power dissipated} = \frac{\pi^3 f^2 \mu^2 N^2 I^2 r^4}{2\rho}$$

$$= \frac{\pi^3 \times 250^2 \times 10^6 \times (4\pi \times 10^{-7})^2 \times 40^2 \times 20^2 \times 50^4}{2 \times 0.05 \times 10^{12}}$$

$$= \underline{122.4 \text{ W per metre length}}$$

Students should check that the assumptions are reasonable.

$$\left| \int_0^r \sigma \overline{E} \, dx \right| \ll NI \text{ if } \frac{\omega \mu r^2}{4\rho} \ll 1$$

For the given figure,

$$\frac{\omega \mu r^2}{4\rho} = 0.025$$

which is $\ll 1$.

### Example 5.2

A semi-infinite slab of semiconductor material shown in the diagram has two identical hemispherical ohmic contacts of radius 1 mm embedded in its surface and set a relatively large distance apart. The resistance and capacitance between the contacts are, respectively, 1 $\Omega$ and 1 pF. Calculate the resistivity and relative permittivity of the semiconductor material.

(CEI Part 2)

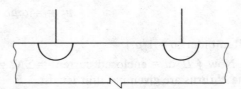

### Solution 5.2

Let the distance between the hemispheres be $D$ and let each be of radius $r$. The capacitance between two hemispheres is given by

$$C = \frac{\pi \epsilon_0 \epsilon_r}{\left[ \dfrac{1}{r} - \dfrac{1}{D-r} \right]} \text{ F}$$

(use the analogue relationship). The resistance between the hemispheres is

$$R = \frac{\rho}{\pi} \left[ \frac{1}{r} - \frac{1}{D-r} \right] \Omega$$

As $C = 1 \times 10^{-12}$ F,

$$10^{-12} = \frac{\pi \times \dfrac{1}{36\pi \times 10^9} \times \epsilon_r}{(10^3 - 0)}$$

$$D \gg r$$

Hence,

$$\underline{\epsilon_r = 36}$$

Similarly, $R$ is given as $1\ \Omega$; therefore,

$$\rho = \frac{1 \times \pi}{10^3 - 0} = 0.003\ 14\ \Omega\text{m}$$

## Example 5.3

A sinusoidal current of angular frequency $\omega$ rad/s flows in a conductor of resistivity $\rho$ and absolute permeability $\mu$. The conductor cross-section is rectangular, of width much greater than its thickness $2b$. Show that the current density $\overline{J}$ at a distance $y$ from the central plane of the conductor (where $\overline{J} = J_0$) is given by

$$\frac{d^2 \overline{J}}{dy^2} + n^2\ \overline{J} = 0$$

where

$$n^2 = -\frac{j\omega\mu}{\rho}$$

Determine $\overline{J}$ in terms of $J_0$, $\omega$, $b$ and the material constants, and hence derive an expression for the power loss per unit surface area of the conductor.

(CEI Part 2)

### Solution 5.3

$$-\frac{\partial \overline{H}_x}{\partial y} \cdot \partial y = \overline{J} \partial y$$

Thus,

$$\frac{\partial \overline{H}_x}{\partial y} = -\overline{J} = +\frac{1}{\rho}\ \overline{E}_z$$

and

$$\frac{\partial \overline{E}_z}{\partial y} \cdot \partial y = -j\omega\mu\ \overline{H}_x\ \partial y$$

Thus,

$$\overline{H}_x = +\frac{j\rho}{\omega\mu}\ \frac{d\overline{J}}{dy}$$

Therefore,

$$\frac{j\rho}{\omega\mu}\ \frac{d^2\overline{J}}{dy^2} = -\overline{J}$$

111

or

$$\frac{\mathrm{d}^2 \overline{J}}{\mathrm{d}y^2} + n^2\, \overline{J} = 0$$

where $n^2 = -(j\omega\mu/\rho)$.

Now $\gamma^2 + n^2 = 0$, or

$$\gamma^2 = \frac{j\omega\mu}{\rho} = (1 + j)\,\frac{\omega\mu}{2\rho}$$

Thus,

$$\gamma = \pm (1 + j) \left(\frac{\omega\mu}{2\rho}\right)^{\frac{1}{2}} = \pm \alpha\,(1 + j)$$

where

$$\alpha = \left[\frac{\omega\mu}{2\rho}\right]^{\frac{1}{2}}$$

The general solution for $\overline{J}$ will be of the form

$$\overline{J} = (Ae^{\gamma y} + Be^{-\gamma y})\,e^{j\omega t} = \frac{\overline{E}_z}{\rho}$$

When $y = 0$, $J_0 = A + B$,

$$\overline{H}_x = \frac{j\gamma\rho}{\omega\mu}\,[Ae^{\gamma y} - Be^{-\gamma y}]\,e^{j\omega t}$$

But $\overline{H}_x(y) = -\overline{H}_x(-y)$, so that $\overline{H}_x(0) = 0$ and $A = B = J_0/2$. Therefore,

$$\overline{E}_z = \frac{J_0\rho}{2}\,[e^{\gamma y} + e^{-\gamma y}]\,e^{j\omega t}$$

$$\overline{H}_x = \frac{j\gamma\rho J_0}{2\omega\mu}\,[e^{\gamma y} - e^{-\gamma y}]\,e^{j\omega t}$$

[Reminder: $\gamma = \alpha\,(1 + j)$ and $\gamma^* = \alpha\,(1 - j)$ is the quadrature relationship between $\overline{E}_z$ and $\overline{H}_x$.]

$$\overline{P} = \overline{E}_x \times \overline{H}_x^*$$

$$= \frac{-J_0\rho}{2}\,[e^{\gamma y} + e^{-\gamma y}]\,\frac{j\gamma^*\rho J_0}{2\omega\mu}\,[e^{\gamma^* y} - e^{-\gamma^* y}]$$

$$= \frac{-\alpha(1 + j)\,J_0{}^2\,\rho^2}{\omega\mu}\left[\frac{\sinh 2\alpha y - j\sin 2\alpha y}{2}\right]$$

If $\overline{P}_r$ = real part of $\overline{E}\,\overline{H}^*$,

$$\overline{P}_r = \frac{-\alpha J_0{}^2\,\rho^2}{2\omega\mu}\,[\sinh 2\alpha y + \sin 2\alpha y]$$

Power loss per unit surface area is

$$P = |2\overline{P}_r|_{y=b} = \frac{\alpha J_0{}^2\,\rho^2}{\omega\mu}\,[\sinh 2\alpha b + \sin 2ab]\ \text{W/m}^2$$

## Example 5.4

With Maxwell's equations as a starting point, develop the wave equation pertaining to a plane electromagnetic wave propagating in a medium of conductivity $\sigma$, relative permittivity $\epsilon_r$ and relative permeability $\mu_r = 1$. Discuss how $\sigma$, $\epsilon_r$ and the angular frequency $\omega$ affect two of the following concepts: (a) the intrinsic imped-ance of the medium to wave propagation, (b) the depth of penetration, (c) the phase velocity.

(CEI Part 2)

### Solution 5.4

Maxwell's equations in differential form for a plane wave are

$$-\frac{\partial \bar{H}_z}{\partial x} = \frac{\epsilon \partial \bar{E}_y}{\partial t} + \sigma \bar{E}_y \tag{i}$$

$$\frac{\partial \bar{H}_y}{\partial x} = \frac{\epsilon \partial \bar{E}_z}{\partial t} + \sigma \bar{E}_z \tag{ii}$$

$$\frac{\partial \bar{E}_z}{\partial x} = \frac{\mu \partial \bar{H}_y}{\partial t} \tag{iii}$$

and

$$\frac{\partial \bar{E}_y}{\partial x} = -\frac{\mu \partial \bar{H}_z}{\partial t} \tag{iv}$$

From these equations,

$$-\frac{\partial^2 \bar{H}_z}{\partial x \partial t} = \frac{1}{\mu} \frac{\partial^2 \bar{E}_y}{\partial x^2} \tag{v}$$

$$-\frac{\partial^2 \bar{H}_z}{\partial x \partial t} = \frac{\epsilon \partial^2 \bar{E}_y}{\partial t^2} + \frac{\sigma \partial \bar{E}_y}{\partial t} \tag{vi}$$

Therefore,

$$\frac{1}{\mu} \frac{\partial^2 \bar{E}_y}{\partial x^2} = \frac{\partial^2 \bar{E}_y}{\partial t^2} + \frac{\sigma \partial \bar{E}_y}{\partial t}$$

If these quantities vary sinusoidally with time, then the general form is

$$\frac{1}{\mu} \frac{\partial^2 \bar{E}}{\partial x^2} = -\omega^2 \epsilon \bar{E} + j\omega \sigma \bar{E}$$

or

$$\frac{\partial^2 \bar{E}}{\partial x^2} = + j\omega (\sigma + j\omega \epsilon) \mu \bar{E} = \gamma^2 \bar{E}$$

where $\gamma^2 = j\omega\mu (\sigma + j\omega\epsilon)$ and $\gamma$ is referred to as the propagation coefficient for the medium and is equal to $(\alpha + j\beta)$.

The solution for $E$ then becomes

$$\bar{E} = E_0 e^{j\omega t} e^{-\gamma x}$$

in the positive $x$ direction; therefore,

$$\bar{E} = E_0 e^{j\omega t} e^{-\alpha x} e^{-j\beta x} = E_0 e^{-\alpha x} e^{j(\omega t - \beta x)}$$

This represents a wave travelling in the positive $x$ direction with a velocity $\omega/\beta$ and which is attenuated by the factor $e^{-\alpha x}$.

(a) For a plane wave in a pure dielectric of permittivity $\epsilon$ and travelling in the $x$ direction, differentiate equation (iv) with respect to distance,

$$\frac{\partial^2 \overline{E}_y}{\partial x^2} = -\frac{\mu \partial}{\partial x}\left(\frac{\partial \overline{H}_z}{\partial t}\right)$$

and from equation (vi), with $\sigma = 0$,

$$\frac{\partial}{\partial t}\left(\frac{\partial \overline{H}_z}{\partial x}\right) = -\frac{\epsilon \partial^2 \overline{E}_y}{\partial t^2}$$

Equating these last two equations,

$$\frac{\partial^2 \overline{E}_y}{\partial t^2} = \frac{1}{\mu \epsilon}\frac{\partial^2 \overline{E}_y}{\partial x^2}$$

This equation relates the space and time variations of the scalar magnitude $\overline{E}_y$ of the electric field intensity and is referred to as a wave equation in $\overline{E}_y$.

If equations (iv) and (vi) are differentiated so that $\overline{E}_y$ can be eliminated, then

$$\frac{\partial^2 \overline{H}_z}{\partial t^2} = \frac{1}{\mu \epsilon}\frac{\partial^2 \overline{H}_z}{\partial x^2}$$

This equation has the same form as the equation for $\overline{E}_y$ above.

Now introduce a quantity $v$, given by

$$v^2 = \frac{1}{\mu \epsilon}$$

Then

$$\frac{\partial^2 \overline{E}_y}{\partial t^2} = v^2 \frac{\partial^2 \overline{E}_y}{\partial x^2}$$

The dimensions of $v$ are seen to be metres per second — that is, a velocity. For free space $v$ is equal to $3 \times 10^8$ m/s

A solution for the above second-order equation can be

$$\overline{E}_y = E_0 \sin(\omega t - \beta x)$$

assuming $\alpha = 0$, and

$$\overline{H}_x = H_0 \sin(\omega t - \beta x)$$

both representing a wave travelling in the positive $x$ direction.

To find how $\overline{H}_z$ and $\overline{E}_y$ are related, recall

$$\frac{\partial \overline{E}_y}{\partial x} = -\mu \frac{\partial \overline{H}_z}{\partial t}$$

Substituting for $\overline{E}_y$ into this relationship by differentiating with respect to $x$ and then integrating with respect to time yields

$$\overline{H}_z = \frac{\beta}{\mu \omega} E_0 \sin(\omega t - \beta x)$$

Taking the ratio between $\overline{E}_y$ and $\overline{H}_z$ and remembering that this work is on a single travelling wave,

$$\frac{\overline{E}_y}{\overline{H}_z} = \frac{E_0}{H_0} = \frac{\mu \omega}{\beta} = \frac{\mu}{\sqrt{(\mu \epsilon)}} = \sqrt{\frac{\mu}{\epsilon}}$$

or

$$\overline{E}_y = \sqrt{\frac{\mu}{\epsilon}} \times \overline{H}_z$$

To compare the electric and magnetic wave expressions, consider

$$\overline{E}_y = E_0 \sin (\omega t - \beta x) \quad \text{N/m}$$

$$\overline{H}_z = \sqrt{\frac{\epsilon}{\mu}} E_0 \sin (\omega t - \beta x) \quad \text{A/m}$$

It is now apparent that $\overline{E}_y$ and $\overline{H}_z$ are identical functions of $x$ and $t$, but their magnitudes differ by a factor $\sqrt{(\mu/\epsilon)}$ or its reciprocal.

Examination of the dimensions of $E_0/H_0$ shows

$$\frac{\text{volts/metre}}{\text{amperes/metre}} = \frac{\text{volts}}{\text{amperes}} = \text{ohms}$$

Thus, $\sqrt{(\mu/\epsilon)}$ has the dimensions of impedance, and it may be written as

$$\eta = \sqrt{\frac{\mu}{\epsilon}}$$

where $\eta$ is called the intrinsic impedance of the medium. For free space

$$\eta = \eta_0 = \sqrt{\frac{4\pi}{10^7} \times \frac{36\pi \times 10^9}{1}} = 120\pi \approx 376.7 \ \Omega$$

If $E$ and $H$ are in time phase, $\eta$ is a pure resistance.

All dielectric materials, however, have some conductivity $\sigma$, and while it may be neglected in many cases, it is necessary to establish a criterion for the cases when it cannot be ignored. From equation (vi) $\sigma$ must be included. The mathematic procedure will be as before.

$$\eta = \sqrt{\frac{j\omega\mu}{\sigma + j\omega\epsilon}} = \sqrt{\frac{\mu}{\epsilon}} \times \frac{1}{1 - j\left(\dfrac{\sigma}{\omega\epsilon}\right)}$$

that is, the intrinsic impedance is now a complex quantity. Hence, the electric and magnetic fields are no longer in time phase.

(b) The depth of penetration $\delta$ is that depth at which the wave travelling in the conductor has been attenuated to $1/e$ of its original value. The amplitude of the wave decreases by a factor of $e^{-\alpha x}$; therefore, when $\alpha x = 1$, the amplitude is $1/e$ of its value at $x = 0$. Hence, when $x = 1$, it means that by definition the depth of penetration is $\delta = 1/\alpha$. In general,

$$\delta = \frac{1}{\omega\left\{ \dfrac{\mu\epsilon}{2}\left[ \left( 1 + \dfrac{\sigma^2}{\omega^2 \epsilon^2} \right)^{\frac{1}{2}} - 1 \right] \right\}^{\frac{1}{2}}}$$

For a good conductor,

$$\alpha = \left[ \frac{\omega\mu\sigma}{2} \right]^{\frac{1}{2}}$$

Thus,

$$\delta = \left[ \frac{2}{\omega\mu\sigma} \right]^{\frac{1}{2}}$$

(c) To develop the phase velocity, consider the propagation coefficient

$$\gamma = \left[ j\omega\mu\sigma\left( 1 + \frac{j\omega\epsilon}{\sigma} \right) \right]^{\frac{1}{2}}$$

and let $\sigma/\omega\epsilon \gg 1$ for a good conductor; then

$$\gamma = [j\omega\mu\sigma]^{\frac{1}{2}} = [\omega\mu\sigma]^{\frac{1}{2}} \, \underline{|+45°}$$

Thus,

$$\alpha = \beta = \left[\frac{\omega\mu\sigma}{2}\right]^{\frac{1}{2}}$$

where $\alpha$ = attenuation coefficient (nepers per unit length) and $\beta$ = phase change coefficient (radians per unit length).

The phase velocity of a wave in a good conductor is

$$\frac{\omega}{\beta} = \left[\frac{2\omega}{\mu\sigma}\right]^{\frac{1}{2}}$$

If $\sigma/\omega\epsilon \ll 1$ for a good dielectric, then the binomial theorem can be used on the expression for $\gamma$ — that is,

$$\gamma = j\omega\sqrt{(\mu\epsilon)} \times \left[1 - j\,\frac{\sigma}{2\omega\epsilon} + \frac{1}{8}\left(\frac{\sigma}{\omega\epsilon}\right)^2 - + \cdots\right]$$

Hence,

$$\alpha = j\omega\sqrt{(\mu\epsilon)} \times \left[-j\cdot\frac{\sigma}{2\omega\epsilon}\right] = \frac{\sigma}{2}\left[\frac{\mu}{\epsilon}\right]^{\frac{1}{2}}$$

Similarly,

$$\beta = \omega\sqrt{(\mu\epsilon)} \times \left[1 + \frac{1}{8}\left(\frac{\sigma}{\omega\epsilon}\right)^2\right]$$

In many cases $\sigma = 0$, so that

$$\beta = \omega(\mu\epsilon)^{\frac{1}{2}}$$

Thus, the effect of a small amount of loss in the dielectric is to add a small correction factor to $\beta$.

The phase velocity is given by

$$v = \frac{\omega}{\beta} = \frac{1}{(\mu\epsilon)^{\frac{1}{2}}\left(1 + \dfrac{\sigma^2}{8\omega^2\epsilon^2}\right)}$$

## Example 5.5

A long conductor, of conductivity $\sigma$ and carrying a current $I$ of angular frequency $\omega$, lies in a slot in a semi-infinite ferromagnetic block of infinite permeability and zero coductivity — see diagram. Assuming the magnetic field strength, $\overline{H}$, in the conductor to be $y$-directed and the electric field strength, $\overline{E}$, to be $z$-directed, apply Maxwell's equations to determine expressions for: (a) $\overline{E}$ and $\overline{H}$, and (b) the impedance of the conductor per unit length when the depth $h$ is much greater than the depth of penetration $\delta = (2/\omega\mu_0\sigma)^{\frac{1}{2}}$.

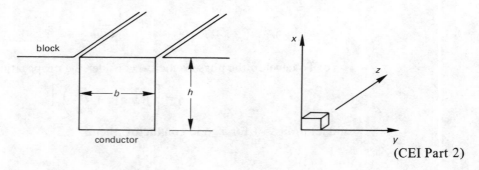

(CEI Part 2)

## Solution 5.5

Assume that the material is a good conductor, so that $\sigma \gg \omega\epsilon_0$ or the current is essentially one of conduction. In the ferromagnetic block $\mu = \infty$, so that magnetic intensity $\bar{H}$ is zero, though the flux density $\bar{B}$ has a finite non-zero value, as shown in the diagram.

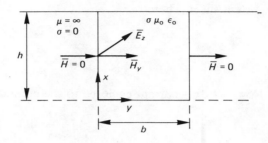

Using Maxwell's equations in matrix form,

$$\begin{vmatrix} u_x & u_y & u_z \\ \partial/\partial_x & \partial/\partial_y & \partial/\partial_z \\ 0 & \bar{H}_y & 0 \end{vmatrix} = u_z[\sigma\bar{E}_z + j\omega\epsilon\bar{E}_z] = u_z\sigma\bar{E}_z$$

$$\begin{vmatrix} u_x & u_y & u_z \\ \partial/\partial_x & \partial/\partial_y & \partial/\partial_z \\ 0 & 0 & \bar{E}_z \end{vmatrix} = -j\omega\mu_0\,\bar{H}_y\,u_y$$

Therefore,

$$\frac{\partial\bar{H}_y}{\partial z} = 0, \quad \frac{\partial\bar{H}_y}{\partial x} = \sigma\bar{E}_z$$

$$\frac{\partial\bar{E}_z}{\partial y} = 0, \quad \frac{\partial\bar{E}_z}{\partial x} = j\omega\mu_0\,\bar{H}_y$$

Div $B = 0$; therefore,

$$\frac{\partial\bar{H}_y}{\partial y} = 0$$

Div $D = 0$; therefore,

$$\frac{\partial\bar{E}_z}{\partial z} = 0$$

Thus, $\bar{H}_y, \bar{E}_z$ vary only with $x$ and time.

$$\frac{\partial^2\bar{E}_z}{\partial x^2} = j\omega\mu_0\,\frac{\partial\bar{H}_y}{\partial x} = j\omega\mu_0\,\sigma\bar{E}_z = \gamma^2\bar{E}_z$$

$$\gamma = \pm(1+j)\sqrt{\left(\frac{\omega\mu_0\sigma}{2}\right)}$$

depth of penetration $\delta = \sqrt{\left(\dfrac{2}{\omega\mu_0\sigma}\right)}$

Thus, $\gamma = \pm(1+j)/\delta$, assuming $h \gg \delta$.

The general solution for the $\bar{E}_z$ equation is of the form

$$\bar{E}_z = Ae^{\gamma x} + Be^{-\gamma x}$$

Hence,

$$\bar{H}_y = \frac{\gamma}{j\omega\mu_0}[Ae^{\gamma x} - Be^{-\gamma x}]$$

At the bottom of the slot $\bar{H}_y$ must be continuous; then at $x = 0$, $\bar{H}_y = 0$ unless there is a current sheet at the bottom of the slot. Hence, $A = B$ if there is no current sheet. Therefore,

$$\bar{E}_z = 2A \cosh \gamma x$$

$$\bar{H}_y = \frac{2\gamma A}{j\omega\mu_0} \sinh \gamma x$$

Now $\oint \bar{H}\, dx = $ current enclosed to the boundary of the conductor; then

$$\frac{2\gamma Ab}{j\omega\mu_0} \sinh \gamma h = I$$

or

$$A = \frac{j\omega\mu_0 I}{2\gamma b \sinh \gamma h}$$

(a) Thus,

$$\underline{\bar{H}_y = \frac{I}{b} \frac{\sinh \gamma x}{\sinh \gamma h}}$$

and

$$\underline{\bar{E}_z = \frac{j\omega\mu_0 I}{\gamma b} \frac{\cosh \gamma x}{\sinh \gamma h}}$$

Note

$$\int_0^h b \sigma \bar{E}_z\, dx = I$$

For $|\gamma h| \gg 1$,

$$\bar{E}_z \text{ (on the surface)} = \frac{j\omega\mu_0}{\gamma b} I$$

(b) The potential difference per unit length equals $\bar{E}_z \times 1$ or $V$ volts per unit length; therefore,

$$\text{impedance } Z = \frac{V}{I} = \frac{j\omega\mu_0}{\gamma b}$$

$$Z = \frac{j\omega\mu_0}{b(1+j)\sqrt{\left(\dfrac{\omega\mu_0\sigma}{2}\right)}}$$

$$= \frac{j\omega\mu_0\delta}{b(1+j)}$$

**Example 5.6**

Explain the boundary conditions which relate the time-varying electric and magnetic fields on the two sides of a boundary between two non-conducting media.

A uniform plane wave is propagated through free space in the $Z$ direction. At $Z = 0$ it is incident on a semi-infinite slab of dielectric of relative permittivity 9.0 which occupies the region $Z \geqslant 0$. If the electric field strength of the incident wave at $Z = 0$ is 20 mV/m, calculate the strength of the magnetic field immediately inside the dielectric.

A sheet of dielectric of thickness 0.04 m and relative permittivity 3.0 is now placed on the surface of the dielectric slab. Calculate the lowest frequency of the propagated wave at which there is no reflection into the free space region.

(Engineering Council Part 2A)

*Solution 5.6*

Boundary relations already discussed for static electric and magnetic fields also hold for time-varying fields. This may be shown by consideration of Figure 1 and a small rectangular section enclosing both media.

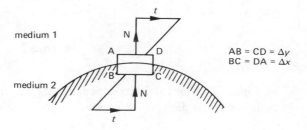

**Figure 1**

Consider first of all an electric field across the two media and the tangential components $\overline{E}_t$ by using Maxwell's equation derived from Faraday's law:

$$\oint \overline{E} \ \mathrm{d}x = - \int_s \frac{\partial \overline{B}}{\partial t} \cdot \mathrm{d}s$$

If there is a flux density $\overline{B}$ normal to the rectangular path and $\overline{B}$ changes with time, then $\oint \overline{E} \cdot \mathrm{d}x$ is not zero if the path encloses a finite area. As $\Delta y \to 0$, then area ABCD $\to 0$ and the surface integral of $\partial \overline{B}/\partial t$ vanishes. Thus, the work around the path is given by

$$\overline{E}_{t1} \ \Delta x - \overline{E}_{t2} \ \Delta x = 0$$

Hence,

$$\overline{E}_{t1} = \overline{E}_{t2}$$

Now consider the tangential components of an $\overline{H}$ field. Use Maxwell's equation derived from Ampere's law in its complex form,

$$\oint \overline{H} \cdot \mathrm{d}x = \int_s \left( \overline{J} + \frac{\partial \overline{D}}{\partial t} \right) \cdot \mathrm{d}s$$

If there is a time-changing $\overline{D}$ normal to the rectangular path ABCD, then there will be a contribution due to $\overline{D}$. As the dimension $\Delta y \to 0$, the surface integral of

$\partial D / \partial t$ will vanish. The conduction current density $\overline{J}$ may also change with time, but its surface integral will also vanish as $\Delta y \to 0$ unless it is assumed that the conduction current exists in an infinitesimally thin layer at the conductor surface. But the two media are of non-conducting material; hence,

$$\overline{H}_{t1} - \overline{H}_{t2} = 0$$

The two media may have any permeabilities or permittivities.

A plane wave in air incident normally on a half space filled with a lossless dielectric medium $\epsilon_r = 9$ will be partially reflected and partially transmitted as shown

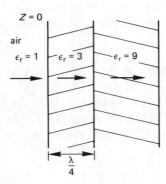

**Figure 2**

in Figure 2. The intrinsic impedance $\eta_0$ for free space = $120\pi \ \Omega$, while the impedance in the dielectric medium,

$$\eta = \frac{120\pi}{\sqrt{9}} = 40\pi \ \Omega$$

Transmission coefficient at boundary $= \dfrac{2 \times \eta}{\eta + \eta_0} = \dfrac{2 \times 40\pi}{40\pi + 120\pi} = \dfrac{1}{2}$

Hence, the transmitted electric field into the dielectric medium

$$= \tfrac{1}{2} \times 20 \ \text{mV/m}$$

$$= 10 \ \text{mV/m}$$

In the medium, $\qquad\qquad \dfrac{\overline{E}}{\overline{H}} = \eta = 40\pi$

Hence, $\qquad\qquad \overline{H} = \dfrac{10 \times 10^{-3}}{40\pi} = \underline{0.08 \ \text{mA/m}}$

To avoid reflection through the dielectric medium, a plate made of a second dielectric material may be inserted (Figure 2) provided that the plate is a quarter of a wavelength thick. This is exactly the same method of *matching* (i.e. no reflection) as in transmission line theory, using a quarter-wavelength line. Evaluate the intrinsic impedance of the plate

$$\eta_0^1 = \sqrt{\eta_0 \times \eta} = \sqrt{4800\pi^2} \ \Omega$$

For a quarter-wavelength the relative permittivity of this plate must equal

$$\left[ \frac{\eta_0}{\eta_0^1} \right]^2$$

i.e.

$$\left[\frac{120\pi}{\sqrt{4800\pi}}\right]^2 = 3 = \epsilon_r$$

Thus, the thickness of the plate becomes

$$0.04 \text{ m} = \frac{\lambda}{4}$$

where $\lambda$ is the wavelength of the plane wave transmission in the medium ($\beta x = \pi/2$).

$$\text{Phase velocity in medium} = \frac{c}{\sqrt{\epsilon_r}} \text{ m/s}$$

$$= \frac{3 \times 10^8}{\sqrt{3}} \text{ m/s}$$

Now $\lambda \times f$ = velocity, or

$$f = \frac{3 \times 10^8}{\sqrt{3} \times 0.16} = 1.0825 \text{ GHz}$$

## Example 5.7

Derive expressions for the electric and magnetic fields within a long cylindrical isolated conductor carrying a sinusoidal current of angular frequency $\omega$. Assume the field penetration to be small compared with the radius of the conductor, and make what further simplifying assumptions are appropriate. Show that for calculating power loss, the resistance per unit length may be taken as

$$\left[\frac{1}{a}\right]\left[\frac{1}{2}\frac{\omega\mu}{\sigma}\right]^{\frac{1}{2}}$$

where $a$ is the perimeter of the conductor, and $\mu$ and $\sigma$ the permeability and conductivity of its material.

(CEI Part 2)

## Solution 5.7

Consider the cylindrical conductor of Figure 1, where vectors $\bar{J}$ and $\bar{E}$ are axial, while $\bar{H}$ is circumferential. A thin cylindrical shell of radius $r$ and thickness $\delta r$ is shown:

$$\text{curved surface area} = 2\pi r \delta r$$

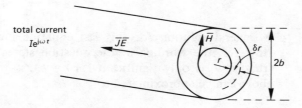

**Figure 1**

Therefore,

$$\text{enclosed current} = 2\pi r\, \delta r\, \bar{J} = \int \bar{H}\, \delta r$$

$$2\pi\,(r + \delta r)\left(\bar{H} + \frac{\mathrm{d}\bar{H}}{\mathrm{d}r}\cdot\delta r\right) - 2\pi r\bar{H} = 2\pi r\,\delta r\,\bar{J}$$

$$\bar{H} + r\,\frac{\mathrm{d}\bar{H}}{\mathrm{d}r} = r\bar{J} = \frac{\mathrm{d}}{\mathrm{d}r}\,(r\bar{H})$$

$$\bar{J} = \frac{1}{r}\,\frac{\mathrm{d}(r\bar{H})}{\mathrm{d}r}$$

From Faraday's law (Figure 2),

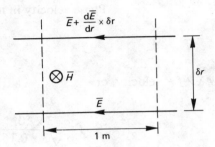

**Figure 2**

$$\bar{E}\times 1 - \left[\bar{E} + \frac{\mathrm{d}\bar{E}}{\mathrm{d}r}\times\delta r\right]\times 1 = -\,\mathrm{j}\omega\mu\bar{H}\delta r\times 1$$

$$\frac{\mathrm{d}\bar{E}}{\mathrm{d}r} = \mathrm{j}\omega\mu\bar{H}$$

also

$$\bar{J} = \sigma\bar{E}$$

This last equation ignores the displacement current for a *good conductor*; hence,

$$\bar{H} = \frac{1}{\mathrm{j}\omega\mu\sigma}\,\frac{\mathrm{d}\bar{J}}{\mathrm{d}r}$$

or

$$\bar{J} = \frac{1}{r}\,\frac{\mathrm{d}}{\mathrm{d}r}\left[\frac{r}{\mathrm{j}\omega\mu\sigma}\,\times\,\frac{\mathrm{d}\bar{J}}{\mathrm{d}r}\right]$$

Thus,

$$\mathrm{j}\omega\mu\sigma\,\bar{J} = \frac{1}{r}\left[\frac{\mathrm{d}\bar{J}}{\mathrm{d}r} + \frac{r\mathrm{d}^2\bar{J}}{\mathrm{d}r^2}\right]$$

$$= \frac{1}{r}\,\frac{\mathrm{d}\bar{J}}{\mathrm{d}r} + \frac{\mathrm{d}^2\bar{J}}{\mathrm{d}r^2}$$

A general solution for this last equation involves the use of Bessel functions. However, the wording of the question states that the field penetration is small (that is, $\bar{J}$ is only significant for $r = b$), so that the second-order equation in $\bar{J}$ above can be approximated to

$$\frac{\mathrm{d}^2\bar{J}}{\mathrm{d}r^2} = \mathrm{j}\omega\mu\sigma\,\bar{J}$$

122

The solution to this equation is of the form

$$\bar{J} = J_0\, e^{\gamma r}$$

where $\gamma^2 = j\omega\mu\sigma$; also

$$\gamma^2 = (1+j)^2\, \frac{\omega\mu\sigma}{2}$$

$$\gamma = (1+j)\,\alpha$$

where

$$\alpha = \left(\frac{\omega\mu\sigma}{2}\right)^{\frac{1}{2}}$$

Therefore,

$$\bar{H} = \frac{1}{\gamma^2}\, \frac{d\bar{J}}{dr} = \frac{J_0}{\gamma}\, e^{\gamma r}$$

When $r = b$,

$$\bar{H} = \frac{J_0}{\gamma}\, e^{\gamma b}$$

and

$$\bar{H} \times 2\pi b = I\, e^{j\omega t}$$

Therefore,

$$J_0 = \frac{\gamma I}{2\pi b}\, e^{-\gamma b}\, e^{j\omega t}$$

Thus,

$$\bar{H} = \frac{I}{2\pi b}\, e^{\gamma(r-b)} e^{j\omega t}$$

and

$$\bar{E} = \frac{\gamma I}{2\pi b\sigma}\, e^{\gamma(r-b)} e^{j\omega t}$$

Since

$$\bar{J} = \frac{\gamma I}{2\pi b}\, e^{\gamma(r-b)}\, e^{j\omega t}$$

at $r = b$ again

$$\bar{H} = \frac{I e^{j\omega t}}{2\pi b}$$

and

$$\bar{E} = \frac{\gamma I e^{j\omega t}}{2\pi b\sigma}$$

as expected.

The Poynting vector $\bar{P} = \bar{E} \times \bar{H}^*$ acts radially inward and

$$p_{\mathrm{r}} = \text{real part of } \bar{E} \times \bar{H}^*$$

$$p_{\mathrm{r}} = \frac{\gamma I^2}{4\pi^2 b^2 \sigma}$$

Integrate this expression over a unit length of surface, where $a$ is the perimeter surface and the power loss to heating is $I^2 R$. Therefore,

$$I^2 R = \frac{I^2}{4\pi^2 b^2 \sigma} \times \alpha \times 2\pi b$$

where $2\pi b = a =$ perimeter and $\alpha =$ real part of $\gamma$.

$$R = \frac{\alpha}{a\sigma} = \frac{1}{a} \left[ \frac{\omega\mu}{2\sigma} \right]^{\frac{1}{2}} \Omega$$

where $R$ is the resistance per unit length.


## Example 5.8

Explain what is meant by *space charge*. Discuss the effect of space charge on the conduction in a planar diode.

Show (a) that the average velocity of an electron in a space-charge-limited diode is one-third of the maximum and (b) that in the absence of space charge the average velocity is one-half of the maximum. Assume in each case that the initial velocity of the electron is zero.

(CEI Part 2)


## Solution 5.8

In a planar diode, electrons emitted by the cathode will be attracted to the anode if this is at positive potential, say $V_0$. If $V_0$ is large, all the emitted electrons will reach the anode (the actual number depends on the cathode temperature), and the resultant diode current is said to be 'temperature-limited', with the potential $V_0$ linearly distributed between the anode and the cathode.

If $V_0$ is a lower value than the above, the slower-moving electrons form a negative space charge, particularly in the region of the cathode, and this results in a modification of the electric field distribution and so controls the current flow. Assuming that the emitted electrons have zero velocity, the electric field is adjusted by the space charge until the limiting distribution is reached, when the field is zero at the cathode and increases to reach its maximum value at the anode. This will give rise to the 'three-halves' power law for the planar diode characteristics.

(a) In the space-charge-limited case the current density $\overline{J}$ will be constant, so that $d\overline{J}/dx = 0$. Alternatively, Div $\overline{J} = 0$, but Div $\overline{J} + (\partial\rho/\partial t) = 0$; therefore, the charge distribution is constant with time. If the electron velocity at any distance $x$ from the cathode is $v$ m/s, then $\overline{J} = \rho v =$ constant. Now

$$\text{Div } \overline{D} = \rho$$

or

$$\epsilon \frac{d\overline{E}}{dx} = \rho = \frac{\overline{J}}{\overline{v}} = -\epsilon \frac{d^2 V}{dx^2}$$

or

$$\frac{d^2 V}{dx^2} = \frac{|\overline{J}|}{\epsilon v}$$

Consider the kinetic energy available, equated to the actual potential energy; then

$$\tfrac{1}{2} m v^2 = eV$$

or

$$v = \sqrt{\frac{2e}{m}} \; V$$

Hence,

$$\frac{d^2 V}{dx^2} = \frac{|\bar{J}|}{\epsilon} \left[\frac{m}{2e}\right]^{\frac{1}{2}} V^{-\frac{1}{2}} = kV^{-\frac{1}{2}}$$

where

$$k = \frac{|\bar{J}|}{\epsilon} \left[\frac{m}{2e}\right]^{\frac{1}{2}}$$

Suggest a solution to be of the form

$$V = V_0 \left[\frac{x}{d}\right]^n$$

where $d$ is the value of $x$ at the anode.

$$\frac{d^2 V}{dx^2} = \frac{V_0}{d^2} \; n(n-1) \left[\frac{x}{d}\right]^{n-2}$$

But

$$\frac{d^2 V}{dx^2} = \frac{k}{V^{\frac{1}{2}}} = \frac{k}{[V_0]^{\frac{1}{2}}} \times \left[\frac{x}{d}\right]^{-\frac{n}{2}}$$

From these last two equations, equate indices to yield $n - 2 = -(n/2)$ or $n = 4/3$. This now satisfies $dV/dx = 0$ at $x = 0$, and gives $k \propto V_0^{3/2}$ — that is, $\bar{J} \propto V_0^{3/2}$. Therefore,

$$v = \left[\frac{2e}{m}\right]^{\frac{1}{2}} \times V_0^{\frac{1}{2}} \times \left[\frac{x}{d}\right]^{\frac{2}{3}}$$

$$v = v_{\max} \times \left[\frac{x}{d}\right]^{\frac{2}{3}}$$

But $v = dx/dt$; therefore,

$$\int_0^{t_{\max}} v_{\max} \, d^{-\frac{2}{3}} \, dt = \int_0^d x^{-\frac{2}{3}} \, dx$$

where $t_{\max}$ is the transit time of the electron. Therefore,

$$v_{\max} \times d^{-\frac{2}{3}} \times t_{\max} = 3 \, d^{\frac{1}{3}}$$

Thus,

$$v_{\max} = 3d/t_{\max} = \underline{3 \times \text{average velocity}}$$

(b) No space charge; therefore,

$$\frac{dV}{dx} = \frac{V_0}{d}$$

so

$$V = V_0 \left(\frac{x}{d}\right)$$

From the velocity equation,

$$v = \left[\frac{2e\,V_0}{m}\right]^{\frac{1}{2}}\left[\frac{x}{d}\right]^{\frac{1}{2}} = v_{\max}\left[\frac{x}{d}\right]^{\frac{1}{2}}$$

but $v = \mathrm{d}x/\mathrm{d}t$; therefore,

$$\int_0^{t_{\max}} v_{\max}\, d^{-\frac{1}{2}}\, \mathrm{d}t = \int_0^d x^{-\frac{1}{2}}\, \mathrm{d}x$$

Therefore,

$$\frac{v_{\max}\, t_{\max}}{d^{\frac{1}{2}}} = 2\, d^{\frac{1}{2}}$$

or

$$v_{\max} = \frac{2d}{t_{\max}} = 2 \times \text{average velocity}$$

### Example 5.9

Power is conveyed along an air-spaced coaxial cable of zero resistance from a direct voltage supply to a resistive load. By means of the Poynting vector determine the power flow through the cable dielectric at any section along it. Discuss the result, and explain how $I^2 R$ losses are supplied if the cable conductors have a finite resistance.

### Solution 5.9

Suppose the core and sheath (see part (a) of diagram) to be loss-free ($\sigma = \infty$) and that a direct current $I$ is carried at voltage $V$. For the concentric cable, charge $q$ C/m, the electric field strength $\overline{E}$ and magnetic field strength $\overline{H}$ are given by

$$\overline{H} = \frac{I}{2\pi x}\ \text{A/m}$$

$$\overline{E} = \frac{q}{2\pi\epsilon x}\ \text{V/m}$$

$$V = \frac{q}{2\pi\epsilon\, \log_e (b/a)}$$

$$\overline{E} = \frac{V}{x\, \log_e (b/a)}$$

$$\overline{P} = \overline{E} \times \overline{H} = \frac{VI}{2\pi x^2\, \log_e (b/a)}\ \text{W/m}^2$$

This is the power density flow along the dielectric towards the load (see part (b) of diagram), so that the total power flow will be found over the circular end, with $x$ varying between the limits $a$ and $b$.

Surface area section $\mathrm{d}s = 2\pi x\, \mathrm{d}x$

$$\text{Power} = \int_s \overline{P}\, \mathrm{d}s = \frac{VI}{2\pi\, \log_e (b/a)} \int_a^b \frac{2\pi x\, \mathrm{d}x}{x^2}\ \text{W}$$

$$= \frac{VI}{\log_e (b/a)}\ [\log x]_a^b = VI\ \text{W, as expected}$$

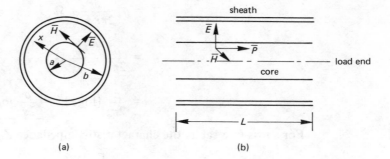

(a)                    (b)

Note that the power appears to flow down the dielectric between core and sheath, which serve only to guide $\bar{P}$ but *not* to carry it.

Now suppose that the core has resistance but not the sheath, and let them be short-circuited at the far end. At the surface of the core $x = a$.

$$\bar{H} = \frac{I}{2\pi a} \text{ A/m}$$

$$\bar{E} = \frac{V}{L} \text{ V/m}$$

The latter relation comes from observing that the whole voltage $V$ is lost in moving down the length $L$, presumed to be uniform. Hence,

$$\bar{P} = \bar{E} \times \bar{H} = \frac{V}{L} \times \frac{I}{2\pi a} = \frac{VI}{2\pi a L} \text{ W/m}^2$$

The power flow must be *into* the core, where it is dissipated as $I^2 R$ losses.

The total power flow *into* the core is

$$P = -\oint_s \bar{P} \cdot \mathrm{d}s = \frac{VI}{2\pi a L} \times 2\pi a L = VI$$

This is as expected and equal to $I^2 R$ in the core. [Remember that it could otherwise be found from $\int_{\text{vol}} \bar{J} \cdot \bar{E} \, \mathrm{d} \text{(vol)}$ in the core.]

### Example 5.10

An annular-shaped resistor is made with inner radius $r$ and outer radius $R$ from resistive sheet material of resistance $\rho$ per square. Find the resistance between the inner and outer circular edges.

Such a resistor is used to provide a matching termination for a loss-free coaxial cable of radii $r$ and $R$. The cable is insulated with polythene (relative permittivity $\epsilon_r = 2.3$). Find the necessary value of $\rho$. Derive any formulae used.

(CEI Part 2)

### *Solution 5.10*

Now

$$\text{current } I = \int_s \bar{J} \cdot \mathrm{d}s \text{ A}$$

$$\text{Resistance} = \frac{\rho \times \text{length}}{\text{area}} = \rho \frac{\mathrm{d}r}{\mathrm{d}s} \Omega$$

$$= \rho \; \frac{dr}{2\pi r \times 1} \; \Omega$$

$$= \frac{\rho}{2\pi} \int_r^R \frac{dr}{r} \; \Omega$$

$$= \frac{\rho}{2\pi} \; [\log r]_r^R = \frac{\rho}{2\pi} \; \log_e \frac{R}{r} \; \Omega$$

For a loss-free cable, the characteristic impedance $Z_0$ is given by

$$Z_0 = \left[ \frac{L}{C} \right]^{\frac{1}{2}} \; \Omega \; \text{(real)}$$

Remember that the analogue between inductance and capacitance from the above expression for resistance is

$$L = \frac{\mu_0}{2\pi} \; \log_e \frac{R}{r} \; \text{H}$$

and

$$C = \frac{2\pi\epsilon_0\epsilon_r}{\log_e \dfrac{R}{r}} \; \text{F}$$

Thus, squaring both sides of the $Z_0$ equation,

$$\frac{\rho^2}{4\pi^2} \; \log_e^2 \left( \frac{R}{r} \right) = \frac{\mu_0}{2\pi} \; \log_e \frac{R}{r} \times \frac{1}{2\pi\epsilon_0\epsilon_r / \log \dfrac{R}{r}}$$

$$\rho^2 = \frac{\mu_0}{\epsilon_0\epsilon_r}$$

Numerical calculation:

$$\rho = \left[ \frac{4\pi \times 36\pi \times 10^9}{10^7 \times 1 \times 2.3} \right]^{\frac{1}{2}} = \underline{248 \; \Omega \text{ per square}}$$

## Example 5.11

A dielectric material of relative permittivity $\epsilon_r$ and loss tangent $\tan \delta$ is subjected to a uniform electric stress of r.m.s. value $\overline{E}$ alternating at angular frequency $\omega$. Show that the specific dielectric loss (power per unit volume) is given by $p = \overline{E}^2 \; \epsilon_0\epsilon_r\omega \tan \delta$.

A concentric cable of inner and outer radii $r = 10$ mm and $R = 20$ mm has an insulant of relative permittivity 3.0. The loss tangent is affected by temperature gradient, and for a given service condition is related to the radius $x$ by $\tan \delta = [1 + (0.005/x)] \times 10^{-3}$. Estimate the dielectric loss for a 1 km length of cable supplied at 150 kV, 50 Hz.

(CEI Part 2)

## Solution 5.11

$$\text{Curl } \overline{H} = \overline{J} + \frac{\partial \overline{D}}{\partial t} = (\sigma + j\omega\epsilon) \; \overline{E}$$

$\overline{J}$ and $\overline{E}$ are in phase and produce power loss per unit volume equal to $p = \overline{J} \times \overline{E} = \sigma \overline{E}^2_{\text{r.m.s.}}$, since $\overline{J} = \sigma \overline{E}$.

$$\text{Loss tangent } \tan \delta = \frac{\sigma}{\omega\epsilon}$$

so that the loss per unit volume due to the conduction current is obtained by substituting for $\sigma$ — that is,

$$p = \omega\epsilon_0\epsilon_r \tan \delta \ \bar{E}^2$$

For the numerical calculation, the insulant has a conductivity $\sigma$, given by

$$\sigma = \omega\epsilon \tan \delta = \omega\epsilon \left[1 + \frac{0.005}{x}\right] \times 10^{-3} \text{ for } r < x < R$$

Let $I$ be the current at radius $x$. Then, for a unit length of cable,

$$\bar{J} \times 2\pi x \times 1 = I = (\sigma + j\omega\epsilon) \bar{E} \ 2\pi x$$

or

$$\bar{E} = \frac{I}{2\pi x (\sigma + j\omega\epsilon)} = \frac{I}{2\pi x \times j\omega\epsilon}$$

as for a dielectric $\sigma \ll \omega\epsilon$.

Now

$$\text{potential } V = - \int_R^r \bar{E} \ dx$$

$$= \frac{I}{2\pi j\omega\epsilon} \int_r^R \frac{dx}{x}$$

$$= \frac{I}{j2\pi\omega\epsilon} \log_e \frac{R}{r}$$

$$= \frac{I}{j2\pi\omega\epsilon} \log_e 2$$

or

$$I = \frac{Vj2\pi\omega\epsilon}{\log_e 2}$$

Therefore,

$$\bar{E} = \frac{Vj2\pi\omega\epsilon}{\log_e 2 \times 2\pi x \times j\omega\epsilon} = \frac{V}{\log_e 2 \times x}$$

$$|E|^2 = \frac{V^2}{(\log_e 2)^2 x^2}$$

$$\text{Power loss } p \text{ per unit length} = \int_r^R \sigma \ |E|^2 \ 2\pi x \ dx$$

$$p = \frac{2\pi V^2}{(\log_e 2)^2} \int_r^R \omega\epsilon \left[1 + \frac{0.005}{x}\right] \times 10^{-3} \times \frac{dx}{x}$$

$$= \frac{2\pi V^2 \ \omega\epsilon}{(\log_e 2)^2} \times 10^{-3} \int_r^R \left(\frac{1}{x} + \frac{0.005}{x^2}\right) dx$$

$$= \frac{2\pi V^2 \ \omega\epsilon}{(\log_e 2)} \times 10^{-3} \left[\log_e 2 + \frac{0.005}{2r}\right]$$

$$p = \frac{2\pi \times 150^2 \times 10^6 \times 2\pi \times 50 \times 1 \times 3 \times 10^{-3}}{(\log_e 2)^2 \times 36\pi \times 10^9} [0.693 + 0.25] \text{ W}$$

$$p = 2.313 \text{ kW}$$

**Example 5.12**

A concentric cable of inner radius $r$ and outer radius $R$ has an insulant of relative permittivity $\epsilon_r$. Derive an expression for the capacitance $C$ of the cable per unit length.

Evaluate $C$ for $r = 0.005$ m, $R = 0.020$ m and $\epsilon_r = 4.0$.

Carefully draw a flux/equipotential curvilinear square plot for the region of the insulant and use it to obtain a comparable numerical value of $C$.

If there are $n$ radial lines in such a plot, what should be the ratio $r_2/r_1$ between the radii of successive equipotential lines forming the outer and inner boundaries of any curvilinear square?

*Solution 5.12*

Let $q$ be the charge on the inner conductor per metre length of cable. Then the flux density at any radius $x$ within the insulant is

$$\bar{D} = \frac{q}{2\pi x} \ \text{C/m}^2$$

The corresponding electric intensity is

$$\bar{E} = \frac{q}{2\pi x \epsilon} \ \text{V/m}$$

Potential difference $V = -\displaystyle\int_R^r \frac{q}{2\pi\epsilon x} \ dx \ \text{V}$

$$= \frac{q}{2\pi\epsilon} \ \log_e \frac{R}{r} \ \text{V}$$

Thus,

$$\text{capacitance } C = \frac{q}{V} = \frac{2\pi\epsilon}{\log_e \left(\dfrac{R}{r}\right)} \ \text{F/m}$$

For the numerical calculation:

$$C = \frac{2\pi \times 1 \times 4}{36\pi \times 10^9 \times \log_e 4} = \underline{160 \ \text{pF}}$$

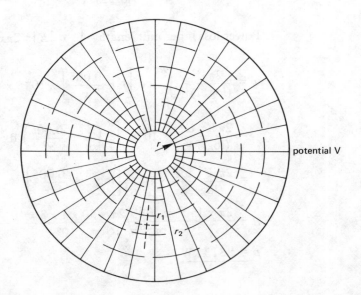

potential V

The curvilinear square plot is shown in the diagram. Tubes of flux $f = 32$; potential steps = 7.

$$\text{Capacitance} = \frac{\epsilon \times f}{p} = \frac{4}{36\pi \times 10^9} \times \frac{32}{7} \text{ F}$$

$$= 162 \text{ pF}$$

Compare with the calculated value, 160 pF.

For the marked curvilinear square for $n$ radial lines,

$$\frac{\pi(r_1 + r_2)}{n} = r_2 - r_1$$

$$r_1(\pi + n) = r_2(n - \pi)$$

$$\frac{r_2}{r_1} = \frac{n + \pi}{n - \pi}$$

# 5.3  Unworked Problems

### Problem 5.1

State Maxwell's equations and briefly explain their physical significance.

Two long and perfectly conducting strips in air form a transmission line as shown in the diagram. Disregarding fringing fields at the strip edges, write down Maxwell equations for the region between the strips and use them to show that

$$\frac{\partial V}{\partial y} = -\mu_0 \left(\frac{s}{b}\right) \frac{\partial I}{\partial t}$$

and

$$\frac{\partial I}{\partial y} = -\epsilon_0 \left(\frac{b}{s}\right) \frac{\partial V}{\partial t}$$

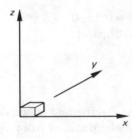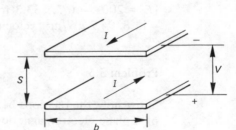

(CEI Part 2)

### Problem 5.2

A wire of circular cross-section is long and straight, and the return path is remote. It carries an alternating current of angular frequency $\omega$, and $\sigma$, $\mu$ and $\epsilon$ are its conductivity, absolute permeability and absolute permittivity. At the operating frequency $\sigma \gg \omega\epsilon$.

Derive the following expression for the current density (complex or $\bar{J}$) in the conductor at any radius $r$:

$$\frac{d^2\bar{J}}{dr^2} + \frac{1}{r}\frac{d\bar{J}}{dr} - j\omega\mu\sigma\bar{J} = 0$$

131

obtaining this expression by Maxwell's equations. The following is the Laplace operator on a vector $\overline{W}$ in cylindrical coordinates $r$, $\theta$, $x$ where there is no variation with $x$ or $\theta$:

$$\frac{1}{r} \frac{\partial}{\partial r} \left( \frac{r \partial \overline{W}}{\partial r} \right)$$

## Problem 5.3

State how Maxwell's electromagnetic field equations are related to the basic experimental laws of electromagnetism.

Evaluate the conduction and displacement current densities $\overline{J}_C$ and $\overline{J}_D$ set up in a uniform isotropic material of conductivity $\sigma$ and absolute permittivity $\epsilon = \epsilon_0 \epsilon_r$ by an electromagnetic field of electric field intensity $\overline{E}$.

A material of conductivity 10 S/m and relative permittivity 1000 (both independent of frequency) lies in an electromagnetic field of frequency $f$. Calculate the ratio $\overline{J}_D / \overline{J}_C$ for frequencies $f$ of 100 Hz and 1000 MHz. Hence, indicate the frequency ranges over which the material can be considered to behave (a) as a conductor, (b) as a leaky dielectric.

$$\left[ \overline{J}_D / \overline{J}_C = \frac{\omega \epsilon}{\sigma} : \frac{5}{9} \times 10^{-6} : \frac{50}{9}; \text{(a) } 0-18 \text{ MHz, (b) } 18 \times 10^9 - 18 \times 10^8 \text{ Hz} \right]$$

## Problem 5.4

An electromagnetic wave with an electric vector $\overline{E} = 200$ mV/m in free space falls normally on to the flat surface of a loss-free solid dielectric material of relative permittivity 4. Proving any formulae used, find the magnitudes of the electric and magnetic field vectors in the incident, reflected and transmitted waves, the corresponding rates of energy flow and the velocity of propagation in the dielectric material.

(IEE Part 3)

$[\overline{E} = 200, -66.7, 133.3 \text{ mV/m}; \overline{H} = 0.53, 0.177, 0.707 \text{ mA/m}; \text{energy flow } 106, -11.8, 94.2 \text{ }\mu\text{W/m}^2; \text{velocity } 1.5 \times 10^8 \text{ m/s}]$

## Problem 5.5

Show how the relations between the electric and magnetic fields and the intensity of a plane electromagnetic wave may be deduced from a study of the propagation of a wave down a parallel plane transmission line, as shown in the diagram.

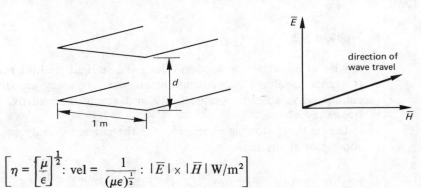

$$\left[ \eta = \left[ \frac{\mu}{\epsilon} \right]^{\frac{1}{2}} : \text{vel} = \frac{1}{(\mu\epsilon)^{\frac{1}{2}}} : |\overline{E}| \times |\overline{H}| \text{ W/m}^2 \right]$$

## Problem 5.6

The intrinsic impedance of free space is $120 \ \pi\Omega$ and a resistive sheet having this resistance is termed a space cloth. Show that the conductivity of such a cloth is $120\pi d$ S/m, where $d$ is the thickness of the sheet.

A uniform plane wave with an electric field strength 10 V/m is incident normally upon an infinite space cloth. Calculate the value of the electric field strength in the transmitted and reflected wave.

What would happen if a perfectly conducting sheet was placed a distance $\lambda/4$ behind the space cloth?

[6.67 V/m; −3.33 V/m; no reflection]

## Problem 5.7

A plane e.m. wave of frequency 1 MHz passes normally into a large flat slab of copper ($\mu_r = \epsilon_r = 1; \sigma = 58$ MS/m) of thickness much greater than the skin depth. The r.m.s. electric field strength of the transmitted wave at the copper surface is 1 V/m. Determine

   (i) the average power flow per unit area at the slab surface,

   (ii) the wave length in the slab, and

   (iii) the electric field strength at a depth of 20 $\mu$m.

(CEI Part 2)

[0.26 mW; 415 $\mu$m; 0.74 V/m]

## Problem 5.8

A plane e.m. wave is directed at an angle $\theta$ to the normal of an extensive and perfectly conducting flat sheet in air, with the electric field perpendicular to the plane of incidence.

   (i) Show that the incident and reflected waves combine to produce a standing wave of electric field strength along the normal.

   (ii) Calculate the wavelength of the standing wave in (i) when the frequency is 1 GHz and $\theta$ is 45°.

[(i) yes; (ii) $\lambda = 0.424$ m]

## Problem 5.9

Consider a $x, y, z$ coordinate origin in free space with the region $z > 0$ being a copper sheet with conductivity $\sigma = 5.73 \times 10^7$ S/m. At the surface there is a tangential electric field strength $\overline{E}$ of value $2 \times 10^{-3} \cos(10^4 t)$ in the $x$ direction.

   (a) Find $\overline{E}, \overline{J}$ and $\overline{H}$ on a plane at $z = 3\delta$.

   (b) Find $\alpha, \beta, \eta, \lambda$ and velocity for a ferrite carrying electromagnetic waves at $10^{10}$ Hz, given $\sigma = 10^{-2}$ S/m, $\epsilon_r = 9$, $\mu_r = 4$.

[(a) $10^{-4} \cos(10^4 t - 3)$ V/m; $5730 \cos(10^4 t - 3)$ A/m$^2$;
$6.73 \cos(10^4 t - 3.785)$ A/m. (b) 1.26; 1260; 251 $(1 - $ j $0.001)$; 5 mm; $0.5 \times 10^8$]

## Problem 5.10

(a) State Maxwell's equations in differential form. With these as a starting point, develop the wave equation for a plane electromagnetic wave propagating in a medium of conductivity $\sigma$, permittivity $\epsilon$ and permeability $\mu$.

(b) A single-frequency plane wave is propagating in a medium for which $\sigma = 10$ S/m, $\epsilon = 1000\,\epsilon_0$ and $\mu = \mu_0$. For what frequency will the conduction current and displacement current densities be equal?

(CEI Part 2)

$[\sigma = \omega\epsilon; f = 180$ MHz$]$

## Problem 5.11

Define the Poynting vector and briefly discuss the field concept of energy flow.

A long transmission line is formed from two parallel conducting strips of air, of width $b$ much greater than the spacing $d$. Determine the power transmitted along the line for a given applied voltage $V$, of frequency such that $d$ is small compared with the free-space wavelength.

(CEI Part 2)

## Problem 5.12

A plane electromagnetic wave of frequency 10 kHz passes normally into a large flat slab of brass (conductivity 15 MS/m) coated with a 0.01 m layer of silver (62 MS/m). Calculate the surface impedance of the silver. Describe the effects of increasing the frequency (i) on the wave propagation through the silver and brass, (ii) on the surface impedance of the silver.

(CEI Part 2)

$[6.8 \times 10^{-5}\ \Omega; \angle 45°]$

## Problem 5.13

Starting from the Maxwell equations, obtain the wave equation for a plane electromagnetic wave in free space. Explain briefly what is meant by the Poynting vector, and show for the plane wave that it leads to a result that could be deduced directly from energy considerations.

(CEI Part 2)

## Problem 5.14

From Maxwell equations derive expressions for the intrinsic impedance and propagation coefficient appropriate to the propagation of electromagnetic waves of angular frequency $\omega$ in a medium of conductivity $\sigma$, permittivity $\epsilon$ and permeability $\mu$. Discuss the characteristic differences in propagation in good conductors and good insulators.

From the intrinsic impedances and attenuation coefficients, compare over the frequency range $f$ from 10 kHz to 10 000 kHz the relative effectiveness of copper and Permalloy sheet, 1 mm thick, in shielding an enclosure from incident electromagnetic waves.

The relevant data are: copper $\sigma = 58$ MS/m, $\epsilon_r = 1$, $\mu_r = 1$; Permalloy $\sigma = 1.2$ MS/m, $\epsilon_r = 1$, $\mu_r = 10^4/f$ (with $f$ in kHz).

(CEI Part 2)

$[$Cu: $8.6 \times 10^{-8}$, $1.8 \times 10^{-26}$; Permalloy: $0.086]$

## Problem 5.15

The shape shown in the diagram is cut from a uniform sheet of conducting material. Each marked square has a conductance of 1 unit between opposite sides. Edge AB is maintained at a potential of 100 units; edge CD is maintained at zero

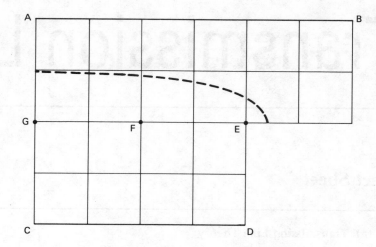

potential. The 75-unit equipotential line is shown dashed. Estimate, by any suitable method, the potentials at E, F and G, and estimate the conductance of the sheet between AB and CD. Sketch in roughly six flow lines.

[66, 52, 50; 1.22]

**Problem 5.16**

The diagram indicates the cross-section of two long conducting cylindrical surfaces of radii 4 and 10 units, respectively. Their axes, though parallel, are displaced by 2 units. Assume that the inner cylinder is held at 4 kV and the outer is earthed.

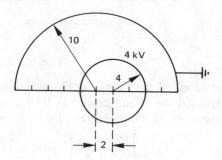

Make a curvilinear field sketch showing equipotentials at 1, 2 and 3 kV. Use the sketch to estimate

   (i) the capacitance per mile, assuming $\epsilon_r = 3$
   (ii) the insulation resistance per mile, assuming $\rho = 10^{12}$ $\Omega$m.

[0.31 $\mu$F/mile; 85 M$\Omega$/mile]

# 6 Transmission Lines

## 6.1 Fact Sheet

### (a) Transmission Line Theory

Figure 6.1 shows a line, of length $l$, having line parameters per unit length of a two-wire line alternatively expressed as 'per loop line length'. The relationship between the current and voltage at any point on the transmission line may be

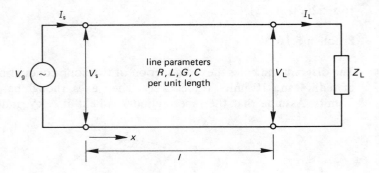

**Fig. 6.1**

obtained in terms of the distributed series impedance $(R + j\omega L)$ $\Omega$ per unit length and a distributed shunt admittance of $(G + j\omega C)$ S per unit length when a generator feeds a load $Z_L$ at a frequency $\omega$ rad/s:

$$V_x = \left[\frac{V_s + I_s Z_0}{2}\right] e^{-\gamma x} + \left[\frac{V_s - I_s Z_0}{2}\right] e^{+\gamma x}$$

$$I_x = \left[\frac{V_s + I_s Z_0}{2Z_0}\right] e^{-\gamma x} + \left[\frac{V_s - I_s Z_0}{2Z_0}\right] e^{+\gamma x}$$

where

$$Z_0 = \left[\frac{R + j\omega L}{G + j\omega C}\right]^{\frac{1}{2}}$$

and

$$\gamma = [(R + j\omega L)(G + j\omega C)]^{\frac{1}{2}}$$

$Z_0$ is the characteristic impedance. $\gamma$ is the propagation constant per unit length and is, in general, complex and written in the form $\gamma = \alpha + j\beta$, where $\alpha$ is the attenuation constant, in nepers per unit length, and $\beta$ is the phase constant, in radians per unit length.

If $\lambda$ is the wavelength on the line, then

$$\lambda = \frac{2\pi}{\beta} \text{ m}$$

and if $v$ is the velocity of propagation of the transmission, then

$$v = \lambda \times f = \frac{\omega}{\beta} \text{ m/s}$$

As an alternative to the exponential form of the voltage and current transmission line equations:

$$V_L = V_s \cosh \gamma l - I_s Z_0 \sinh \gamma l$$

$$I_L = I_s \cosh \gamma l - \frac{V_s}{Z_0} \sinh \gamma l$$

If the problem is considered from the load end of the line, $x$ may be taken as negative; then

$$V_s = V_L \cosh \gamma l + I_L Z_0 \sinh \gamma l$$

$$I_s = I_L \cosh \gamma l + \frac{V_L}{Z_0} \sinh \gamma l$$

*Input impedance* to the line is

$$Z_s = Z_{\text{input}} = \frac{V_s}{I_0} = Z_0 \left[ \frac{Z_L \cosh \gamma l + Z_0 \sinh \gamma l}{Z_0 \cosh \gamma l + Z_L \sinh \gamma l} \right]$$

From these equations, it is clear that the reflection wave will disappear and the line is said *to be matched* when $Z_0 = Z_L$, also $Z_0 = Z_s$. The transmission line equations reduce to the simple form of

$$V_L = V_s e^{-\gamma l}$$

$$I_L = I_s e^{-\gamma l}$$

and

$$V_s = V_L e^{+\gamma l}$$

$$I_s = I_L e^{+\gamma l}$$

This expression represents a rotating vector showing the diminishing value of voltage $|V_s e^{-\alpha x}|$ and rotating through an angle $-\beta x$, lagging because of the negative sign.

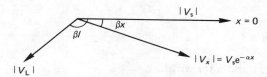

Fig. 6.2

The *voltage reflection coefficient* is defined as the ratio between the reflected voltage and the forward or incident wave at the receiving end. Hence,

$$\rho = \frac{Z_L - Z_0}{Z_L + Z_0}$$

The corresponding *current reflection coefficient* is

$$\rho_i = - \frac{[Z_L - Z_0]}{[Z_L + Z_0]} = - \rho$$

while the *voltage transmission coefficient* is defined as the ratio between the voltage at the line termination and the forward voltage, and is equal to $(1 + \rho)$.

## (b) The Standing Wave Ratio

From the transmission line equations it is evident that, at certain points on the line, the incident and reflected waves will be either in phase or in anti-phase to each other.

At some points maximum voltages will occur, and at quarter-wavelength distances from such voltage maxima, the phases of the two terms will change by $\pi/2$ rad in opposite directions and at these points minimum voltages will occur.

The ratio between maximum voltage and minimum voltage is known as the standing wave ratio, and equals

$$\frac{|V_{max}|}{|V_{min}|} = \frac{1 + |\rho|}{1 - |\rho|}$$

## 6.2 Worked Examples

### Example 6.1

A single-phase transmission line 10 miles long has the following parameters:

> resistance per loop mile 50 $\Omega$
> inductance per mile 0.001 H
> capacitance per mile 0.06 $\mu$F

The shunt conductance may be neglected.

Calculate the characteristic impedance of the line. If the impedance of the load is equal to the characteristic impedance of the line and a potential difference of 5 V at a frequency of 5000 rad/s is applied at the sending end, calculate

    (i) the magnitude of the load current,
    (ii) the wavelength on the line,
    (iii) the velocity of propagation.

### Solution 6.1

Note the parameter wording

$$Z_0 = 10^3 \left[ \frac{50 + j\,5000 \times 0.002}{j\,5000 \times 0.03} \right]^{\frac{1}{2}}$$

$$= 10^3 \left[ \frac{50 + j\,10}{j\,150} \right]^{\frac{1}{2}}$$

$$= \underline{583 \angle -39.3^\circ\ \Omega}$$

Now $\quad \gamma = [(50 + j\,10)\,j\,150 \times 10^{-6}]^{\frac{1}{2}} = 0.0875 \angle 50.65^\circ$

$\gamma l = 0.554 + j\,0.677$

[Reminder: $\alpha$ and $\beta$ must be positive.] Since the line is matched, $Z_L = Z_0$; $I_L = I_s\,e^{-\gamma l}$; and $V_L = V_s\,e^{-\gamma l}$. Therefore,

$$V_L = 5 \angle 0^\circ\,e^{-0.554}\,e^{-j\,0.677} = 2.87 \angle -38.79^\circ$$

Therefore,

$$I_L = \frac{2.87}{583} \frac{\angle -38.79°}{\angle -39.3°} = \underline{4.92 \angle 0.51° \text{ mA}}$$

$$\text{Wavelength } \lambda = \frac{2\pi}{0.0677} = \underline{92.8 \text{ miles}}$$

$$\text{Velocity of propagation} = \frac{5000}{0.0677}$$

$$= \underline{73\,855 \text{ miles/s}}$$

## Example 6.2

A low-loss line has the following parameters:

$$R = 0.014 \ \Omega$$

$$L = 7.2 \times 10^{-9} \ \text{H}$$

$$C = 0.154 \ \mu\mu\text{F}$$

Conductance negligible — all parameters per loop metre.

If the frequency is 200 MHz, what will be the impedance at the input end if the line is exactly one quarter-wavelength and the receiving end is short-circuited?

### Solution 6.2

$l = \lambda/4$ and $\lambda = 2\pi/\beta$. Therefore, $\beta l = \pi/2$. The propagation coefficient is given by

$$\gamma = [(R + j\omega L) \ j\omega C]^{\frac{1}{2}}$$

but, as the frequency is high, this expression may be expanded, using the binomial theorem, to

$$\gamma = \frac{R}{2L} (LC)^{\frac{1}{2}} + j\omega (LC)^{\frac{1}{2}}$$

Therefore,

$$\alpha = \frac{R}{2L} (LC)^{\frac{1}{2}}$$

and

$$\beta = \omega (LC)^{\frac{1}{2}}$$

Therefore,

$$l = \frac{\pi}{2\omega (LC)^{\frac{1}{2}}}$$

giving

$$\alpha l = \frac{\pi R}{4\omega L}$$

From the input impedance equation, with the far end on short-circuit ($Z_L = 0$),

$$Z_{SC} = Z_0 \left[ \frac{Z_0 \ \sinh \gamma l}{Z_0 \ \cosh \gamma l} \right]$$

$$Z_{SC} = Z_0 \tanh [\alpha l + j\beta l]$$

or

$$Z_{\text{SC}} = Z_0 \tanh \left[ \alpha l + j\, \frac{\pi}{2} \right]$$

Now it is necessary to expand the tanh function:

$$Z_{\text{SC}} = Z_0 \left[ \frac{\sinh 2\alpha l + j \sin \pi}{\cosh 2\alpha l + \cos \pi} \right]$$

$$= Z_0 \left[ \frac{\sinh 2\alpha l}{\cosh 2\alpha l - 1} \right]$$

$$= \frac{Z_0}{\tanh \alpha l}$$

Therefore,

$$Z_{\text{SC}} = \left[ \frac{R + j\omega L}{j\omega C} \right]^{\frac{1}{2}} \coth \frac{\pi R}{4\omega L}$$

$$= \left[ \frac{0.014 + j2\pi \times 200 \times 10^6 \times 7.2 \times 10^{-9}}{j2\pi \times 200 \times 10^6 \times 0.154 \times 10^{-12}} \right]^{\frac{1}{2}} \coth 0.001\,22\ \Omega$$

$$= 216.26 \coth 0.001\,22\ \Omega$$

$$= \underline{180\,217\ \Omega}$$

## Example 6.3

The impedance of a telephone line is measured with the far end on open circuit and found to be $750\ \angle 57°\ \Omega$, and with the far end short-circuited $480\ \angle -63°\ \Omega$. Calculate the input voltage needed to supply 2 mW to a resistive load of 300 $\Omega$.

### Solution 6.3

From the input impedance equation and the information that on open circuit $Z_{\text{L}} = \infty$ and on short-circuit $Z_{\text{L}} = 0$, then

$$Z_{\text{OC}} = \frac{Z_0}{\tanh \gamma l}$$

and

$$Z_{\text{SC}} = Z_0 \tanh \gamma l$$

giving

$$Z_0 = [Z_{\text{OC}} \times Z_{\text{SC}}]^{\frac{1}{2}}$$

and

$$\tanh \gamma l = \left[ \frac{Z_{\text{SC}}}{Z_{\text{OC}}} \right]^{\frac{1}{2}}$$

Therefore,

$$Z_0 = [750\ \angle 57° \times 480\ \angle -63°]^{\frac{1}{2}} = 600\ \angle -3°\ \Omega$$

$$\tanh \gamma l = \left[ \frac{480\ \angle -63°}{750\ \angle 57°} \right]^{\frac{1}{2}} = 0.8\ \angle -60°$$

Using the hyperbolic relationships,

$$\cosh \gamma l = \frac{1}{[1 - \tanh^2 \gamma l]^{\frac{1}{2}}}$$

$$= \frac{1}{1 - 0.64 \angle -120°}$$

$$= 0.836 \angle -11.38°$$

Similarly,

$$\sinh \gamma l = 0.669 \angle -71.38°$$

It must be remembered that $\alpha$ and $\beta$ have to be positive – hence, the angles must be corrected for both $\cosh \gamma l$ and $\sinh \gamma l$ – that is,

$$\cosh \gamma l = 0.836 \angle 168.62°$$

and

$$\sinh \gamma l = 0.669 \angle 108.62°$$

Now power $= I_L^2 R$; therefore,

$$I_L = \left[\frac{2 \times 10^{-3}}{300}\right]^{\frac{1}{2}} = 2.58 \text{ mA}$$

Hence,

$$V_L = 300 \times 2.58 \times 10^{-3} = 0.775 \text{ V}$$

Therefore,

$$V_S = 0.775 \times 0.836 \angle 168.6°$$

$$+ 2.58 \times 10^{-3} \times 600 \angle -3° \times 0.669 \angle 108.6°$$

$$= -0.635 + j0.128 - 0.278 + j0.997$$

$$= -0.913 + j1.125$$

$$= \underline{1.45 \angle 129.1° \text{ V}}$$

**Example 6.4**

A loss-free transmission line of characteristic impedance 50 $\Omega$ is terminated at one end in a short-circuit and at the other end in a resistive impedance of 85 $\Omega$. See the diagram. The impedance measured at the junction AA′ is found to be 75 $\Omega$, resistive, at a frequency of 44 MHz. Calculate the phase velocity in the transmission line.

(CEI Part 2)

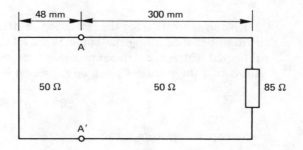

141

*Solution 6.4*

For a loss-free line, $\alpha = 0$; hence,

$$Z_{input} = Z_0 \left[ \frac{Z_L + j\,Z_0\,\tan\beta l}{Z_0 + j\,Z_L\,\tan\beta l} \right]$$

On short-circuit

$$Z_L = 0$$

$$Z_{input} = j\,Z_0\,\tan\beta l$$

$$Z_{SC} = j\,50\,\tan\beta \times 0.048$$

Similarly, for the 300 mm line,

$$Z_{input} = 50 \left[ \frac{85 + j50\,\tan 0.3\beta}{50 + j85\,\tan 0.3\beta} \right]$$

The parallel combination of these two impedances is 75 $\Omega$. However, it is easy to work this problem out in admittance rather than in impedance:

$$\frac{1}{75} = \frac{-j}{50\,\tan\beta 0.048} + \frac{1}{50} \left[ \frac{50 + j85\,\tan 0.3\beta}{85 + j50\,\tan 0.3\beta} \right]$$

$$\frac{1}{75} = \frac{-j}{50\,\tan\beta 0.048} + \left[ \frac{1 + j1.7\,\tan 0.3\beta}{85^2 + 50^2\,\tan^2 0.3\beta} \right] \left[ 85 - j50\,\tan 0.3\beta \right]$$

Equate real terms on both sides:

$$\frac{1}{75} = 85 \left[ \frac{1 + \tan^2 0.3\beta}{85^2 + 50^2\,\tan^2 0.3\beta} \right]$$

Therefore,

$$85^2 + 50^2\,\tan^2 0.3\beta = 75 \times 85 + 75 \times 85\,\tan^2 0.3\beta$$

$$3875\,\tan^2 0.3\beta = 850$$

$$\tan^2 0.3\beta = 0.219$$

$$\tan 0.3\beta = 0.4683$$

$$0.3\beta = 25.096$$

$$\beta = 83.65 \times \frac{\pi}{180} = 1.46 \text{ rad}$$

$$\text{Velocity of propagation} = \frac{\omega}{\beta} = \frac{2\pi \times 44 \times 10^6}{1.46} \text{ m/s}$$

$$= \underline{1.89 \times 10^8 \text{ m/s}}$$

**Example 6.5**

Derive an expression for the reflection coefficient $\rho$ in terms of load and characteristic impedance, using the complexors $V^+$ and $V^-$ representing the forward and reflected voltage coefficients instead of the usual complex parameters. Hence show that the voltage $V_x$ can be expressed in the form

$$V^+ \angle 0° + |\rho| \angle \left( \theta° - \frac{4\pi x°}{\lambda} \right)$$

when operating from the load end.

(Leeds Polytechnic)

**Solution 6.5**

Now, in complexor form,

$$V_x = V^+ \, e^{+\gamma x} + V^- \, e^{-\gamma x}$$

where

$$V^+ = \frac{V_L + I_L Z_0}{2} \quad \text{and} \quad V^- = \frac{V_L - I_L Z_0}{2}$$

and

$$I_x = \frac{V^+}{Z_0} \, e^{\gamma x} - \frac{V^-}{Z_0} \, e^{-\gamma x}$$

where $\gamma$ is the propagation coefficient per unit length of line and $Z_0$ is the characteristic impedance.

At the load $x = 0$

$$V_L = V^+ + V^-$$

and

$$I_L = \frac{V^+}{Z_0} - \frac{V^-}{Z_0}$$

By adding these equations together,

$$2 \, V^+ = V_L + I_L \, Z_0$$

and by subtraction,

$$2 \, V^- = V_L - I_L \, Z_0$$

By definition, the reflection coefficient is the ratio between the reflection voltage wave and the forward voltage wave.

In the general case

$$\rho = \frac{V^- \, e^{-\gamma x}}{V^+ \, e^{+\gamma x}} = \frac{V^-}{V^+} \, e^{-2\gamma x}$$

[Note the exponential index of $-2\gamma x$.] At the load where $x = 0$,

$$\rho = \frac{V^-}{V^+} = \frac{Z_L - Z_0}{Z_L + Z_0}$$

[Reminder: $\rho$ will normally be complex – that is $|\rho| \angle \theta$; therefore,

$$V_x = V^+ \, e^{+\gamma x} + \rho V^+ \, e^{-\gamma x}]$$

$$I_x = \frac{V^+}{Z_0} \, e^{+\gamma x} - \frac{\rho V^+}{Z_0} \, e^{-\gamma x}$$

Also

$$\frac{V^+}{I^+} = + Z_0 \quad \text{and} \quad \frac{V^-}{I^-} = - Z_0$$

Therefore, $I^- = - \rho I^+$ – that is, current reflection coefficient equal and opposite to that of the voltage. Note also that $I_L = I^+ + I^-$.

For a loss-free line $e^{\pm \gamma x}$ becomes $e^{\pm j\beta x}$; therefore,

$$V_x = V^+ \, [e^{+j\beta x} + |\rho| \angle \theta \, e^{-j\beta x}]$$

$$V_x = V^+ \, [\angle \beta x + |\rho| \angle (\theta - \beta x)]$$

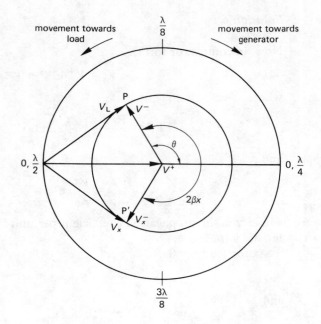

Draw a vector diagram; taking the forward $V^+$ as reference, then, to maintain the correct phase position between $V^+$ and $V^-$, the reflected wave rotates through twice $\beta x$. See diagram. Therefore,

$$V_x = V^+ [\angle 0 + |\rho| \angle \theta - 2\beta x]$$

but $\beta = 2\pi/\lambda$; therefore,

$$V_x = V^+ [\angle 0 + |\rho| \angle \theta - \frac{4\pi x}{\lambda}]$$

Note that the first maximum voltage occurs when $\theta = 2\beta x$, while the first minimum voltage from the load occurs when $\theta + 180 = 2\beta x$ for this particular diagram.

## Example 6.6

A high-frequency transmission line of negligible loss has a characteristic impedance of 600 $\Omega$. Estimate the current standing wave ratio when the load is $(500 + j300)$ $\Omega$.

### Solution 6.6

$$\text{current standing wave ratio} = \frac{|I_{max}|}{|I_{min}|}$$

$$S_i = \frac{1 + |\rho_i|}{1 - |\rho_i|}$$

$$\rho_i = \frac{Z_0 - Z_L}{Z_0 + Z_L} = \frac{600 - 500 - j300}{600 + 500 + j300} = \frac{1 - j3}{11 + j3}$$

$$= 0.284 \angle -86.82°$$

$$S_i = \frac{1 + 0.284}{1 - 0.284} = 1.79$$

**Example 6.7**

A line of characteristic impedance $600 \angle 0°$ $\Omega$ is terminated in a load $Z_L$. The V.S.W.R. measured on the line is 1.5 and the first maximum occurs at 20 cm from the load. The line is open-wire and is supplied from a generator at 300 MHz. Find the value of the load impedance.

*Solution 6.7*

Since the line is open-wire, it can be assumed that the velocity of propagation is $3 \times 10^8$ m/s; hence,

$$3 \times 10^8 = \lambda \times 300 \times 10^6$$

or $\lambda = 1$ m. Therefore, the length of 20 cm is equivalent to $0.2\lambda$; thus, $x = 0.2\lambda$, where the first voltage maximum occurs:

$$|\rho| = \frac{1.5 - 1}{1.5 + 1} = 0.2$$

while the angle is obtained from

$$\theta = 2\beta x = \frac{4\pi}{\lambda} \times 0.2\lambda = 0.8\pi$$

$$\theta = 144°$$

This positive angle indicates that the reflected wave leads the forward wave at the load by 144°. Therefore,

$$0.2 \angle 144° = \frac{Z_L - 600}{Z_L + 600}$$

$$Z_L[1 + 0.162 - j\,0.117] = 600[-0.162 + j\,0.117 + 1]$$

$$Z_L = 600 \left[ \frac{0.838 + j\,0.117}{1.162 - j\,0.117} \right]$$

$$= \frac{600 \times 0.846 \angle 8°}{1.168 \angle -5.75°}$$

$$= 434.6 \angle 13.75°$$

$$\underline{Z_L = (422 + j\,103.3)\ \Omega}$$

**Example 6.8**

An open-wire line with $Z_0 = 700$ $\Omega$ is joined in series with a cable having a characteristic impedance of 80 $\Omega$. If, as a result of connecting a direct voltage to the line, a steep-fronted voltage wave of 1.4 kV travels along it, determine the voltage and current in the cable and open-wire line immediately after the travelling wave has reached the junction. Assume that the lines are loss-free and sufficiently long not to create reflected waves from the far ends.

(IEE Part 3)

*Solution 6.8*

This is a problem involving the effect of an impedance discontinuity, and is worked out from first principles, using complexor notation, together with a small

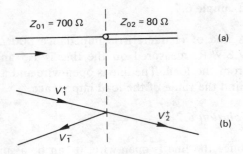

$Z_{01} = 700\ \Omega$  (a)

$Z_{02} = 80\ \Omega$

$V_1^+$

$V_2^+$  (b)

$V_1^-$

Bewley ladder diagram which illustrates the forward and reflected waves involving time and distance, as shown.

$$V_2^+ = V_1^+ + V_1^- \quad \text{and} \quad I_2^+ = I_1^+ + I_1^-$$

Also

$$\frac{V_1^+}{I_1^+} = +Z_{01}\ ;\quad \frac{V_1^-}{I_1^-} = -Z_{01}$$

$$\frac{V_2^+}{I_2^+} = +Z_{02}\ ;\quad \frac{V_2^-}{I_2^-} = -Z_{02}$$

although the last equation is not required in this problem.

By substitution,

$$V_2^+ = \left[\frac{2Z_{02}}{Z_{01} + Z_{02}}\right] V_1^+$$

$$I_2^+ = \left[\frac{2Z_{01}}{Z_{01} + Z_{02}}\right] I_1^+$$

$$V_1^- = \left[\frac{Z_{02} - Z_{01}}{Z_{02} + Z_{01}}\right] V_1^+$$

(Note that the bracket term in this last equation is the reflection coefficient $\rho$.)

$$I_1^- = -\left[\frac{Z_{02} - Z_{01}}{Z_{02} + Z_{01}}\right] I_1^+$$

Inserting the numerical data,

$$V_2^+ = \left[\frac{2 \times 80}{700 + 80}\right] 1.4 = \underline{0.29\ \text{kV}}$$

$$I_2^+ = \left[\frac{2 \times 700}{700 + 80}\right] \frac{1.4 \times 10^3}{700} = \underline{3.59\ \text{A}}$$

Therefore, $V_1^- = -1.11$ kV, a drop in pressure, while $I_1^+ = 2$A; thus, a rise in current occurs after the surge reaches the junction. This is expected, as the impedance falls from 700 $\Omega$ to 80 $\Omega$.

### Example 6.9

A line with a characteristic impedance of 600 $\Omega$ has a load consisting of a 5 k$\Omega$ resistance in parallel with a 0.005 $\mu$F capacitor connected across the far end. A surge voltage of magnitude 5 kV and unit function form travels along the line (see diagram). Derive an expression for the time variation of the voltage across the

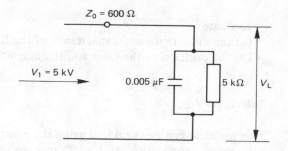

$$Z_0 = 600\ \Omega$$

$V_1 = 5\ \text{kV}$

0.005 $\mu$F    5 k$\Omega$    $V_L$

load, and calculate the value of this voltage 10 $\mu$s after the arrival of the wave front of the surge.

(CEI Part 2)

### Solution 6.9

Express the parallel combination of impedance at the load in the form

$$\frac{5000}{1 + s25}$$

Work out the problem with time in $\mu$s.

$$\text{Voltage across the load} = \frac{2\ \dfrac{5000}{(1 + s25)}}{600 + \dfrac{5000}{(1 + s25)}} \times \frac{5000}{s}$$

$$V_L(s) = \frac{10^4}{s\,(3s + 1.12)} = \frac{10^4/3}{s\,(s + 0.373)}$$

From Laplace transform tables

$$V_L(t) = \frac{10}{3 \times 0.373}\ (1 - e^{-0.373t})\ \text{kV}$$

$$= 8.94\,(1 - e^{-0.373t})\ \text{kV}$$

When $t = 10$,

$$V_L = 8.94\,(1 - e^{-3.73}) = 8.94\,(1 - 0.024)\ \text{kV}$$

$$\underline{V_L = 8.725\ \text{kV}}$$

### Example 6.10

A two-conductor loss-free transmission line, 15 km long, is terminated by a 400 $\Omega$ resistor. A leakage fault between conductors develops at a point on the line. To locate it, a rectangular pulse is applied to the sending end at time $t = 0$. A record of the transmitted pulse and of the first two reflections is shown in the diagram.

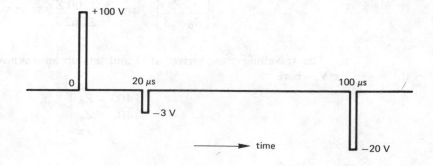

+100 V

0    20 $\mu$s    −3 V    100 $\mu$s    −20 V

time

147

Evaluate
(a) the inductance and capacitance of the line per unit length,
(b) the position of the fault and the magnitude of its conductance.

(CEI Part 2)

### Solution 6.10

This problem can be evaluated using the complexor notation. Loss-free line gives a velocity of propagation of $3 \times 10^8$ m/s, so in 20 $\mu$s a pulse travels 6 km. Hence, the fault is 3 km down the line and the $-3$ V is the reflected voltage from the fault point.

Let the parallel combination of the fault resistance and the line impedance $Z_0$ at point P be $Z$ (see diagram).

$$Z = \frac{RZ_0}{R + Z_0}$$

and, from the reflection coefficient relationship,

$$-3 = \left[ \frac{Z - Z_0}{Z + Z_0} \right] \times 100$$

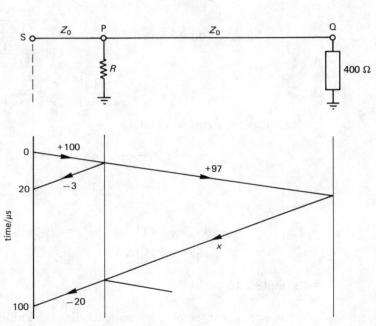

Therefore, $1.03Z = 0.97Z_0$ or $Z_0 = 1.062Z$. The transmitted voltage beyond P is given by

$$\left[ \frac{2Z}{Z_0 + Z} \right] \times 100 = \frac{200\,Z}{2.062\,Z} = 97 \text{ V} \quad \text{(Check.)}$$

The travelling pulse arrives at Q and sets up an unknown reflection wave, say $x$ V, where

$$x = \left[ \frac{400 - Z_0}{400 + Z_0} \right] \times 97$$

Transmitted beyond P towards point S is $-20$ V and this is equated to

$$-20 = \left[\frac{2Z}{Z + Z_0}\right] x = 0.97x$$

Therefore, $x = -20.62$ V, so

$$-20.62 \,(400 + Z_0) = (400 - Z_0) \times 97$$

$$(97 - 20.62)\, Z_0 = 400\,(97 + 20.62)$$

$$76.38\, Z_0 = 47\,048$$

$$Z_0 = 616\ \Omega$$

Therefore,

$$Z = \frac{Z_0}{1.062} = \frac{616}{1.062} = 580\ \Omega$$

Hence,

$$580 = \frac{R \times 616}{R + 616}$$

$$R + 616 = \frac{616}{580} \times R = 1.062R$$

$$0.062\, R = 616 \text{ or } R = 9935.48\ \Omega$$

$$\underline{\text{Conductance of the fault} = 0.1 \text{ mS}}$$

For a loss-free line

$$Z_0 = \left[\frac{L}{C}\right]^{\frac{1}{2}} = 616\ \Omega$$

or

$$L = 379\,456C$$

$$\text{Velocity of propagation} = 3 \times 10^8 = \frac{1}{[LC]^{\frac{1}{2}}}$$

$$9 \times 10^{16} = \frac{1}{LC}$$

Therefore,

$$C = \frac{1}{3 \times 10^8 \times 616} \quad \text{F} = \underline{5.41 \text{ pF/m}}$$

Therefore,

$$L = \frac{379\,456 \times 5.41}{10^{12}} = \underline{2.053\ \mu\text{H/m}}$$

**Example 6.11**

(a) A length $l$ of a transmission line with a propagation coefficient $\gamma = (\alpha + j\beta)$ per unit length is terminated in an impedance $Z$. Develop an expression for the input impedance of the line.

(b) A loss-free transmission line has a characteristic impedance of 50 $\Omega$. A section of the line of length one-eighth of a wavelength is terminated in a load impedance $Z_1$ and its measured input impedance is $(20 - j10)$ $\Omega$. What is the value of $Z_1$?

(CEI Part 2)

### Solution 6.11

Part (a) of this question is book-work and notes will be found at the beginning of the chapter.

A Smith chart can be used for part (b) (see diagram).

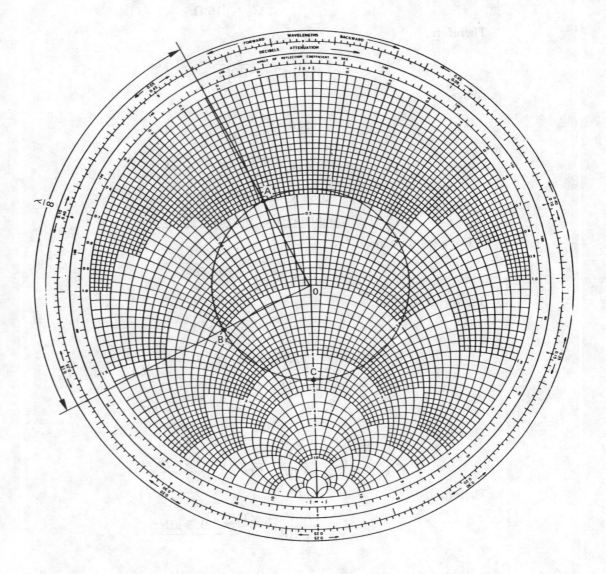

The normalised input impedance is

$$\frac{20 - j10}{50} = 0.4 - j0.2$$

This is point A on the chart. Next draw a circle of radius OA on the chart and then move $\lambda/8$ along the circle circumference towards the load (anticlockwise), point B.

Read off the normalised impedance at this point $1 - j1$; therefore, the load impedance $Z_1$ is

$$Z_1 = 50 (1 - j1) = \underline{(50 - j50)\ \Omega}$$

[Other information from the chart is the V.S.W.R. = 2.6 point C, while the reflection coefficient $\rho = 0.44$.]

**Example 6.12**

The diagram shows a 300 $\Omega$ open-wire line AB branching into two 600 $\Omega$ lines BC and BD. Branch BC, of length 0.175$\lambda$, feeds a load of $(360 + j0)\ \Omega$, while branch BD, of length 0.06$\lambda$, is terminated in an impedance of $(390 - j480)\ \Omega$. Making use of the Smith chart, determine the V.S.W.R. on the 300 $\Omega$ line.

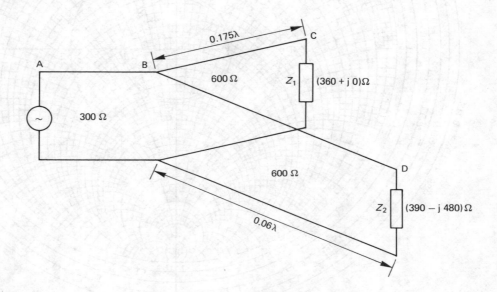

Determine also the length and position of a short-circuited 300 $\Omega$ stub line that will improve the standing wave ratio on AB to unity.

(CEI Part 2)

**Solution 6.12**

Consider the diagram and commence with branch BC — normalise the load:

$$Z_1 = \frac{360}{600} = 0.6$$

which is point A on the chart. Draw a circle radius OA and obtain the corresponding load admittance, point B: $Y_1 = 1.7$. Move 0.175$\lambda$ towards the generator, which yields $Y_{11} = 0.69 - j0.29$, point C.

Now for branch BD, and normalise the load:

$$Z_2 = \frac{390 - j480}{600} = 0.65 - j0.8$$

which is point D on the chart. Draw a circle OD and obtain the load admittance $Y_2 = 0.62 + j0.76$, point E. Move 0.06$\lambda$ towards the generator along the circle circumference, to give $Y_{22} = 1.35 + j1.25$, point F.

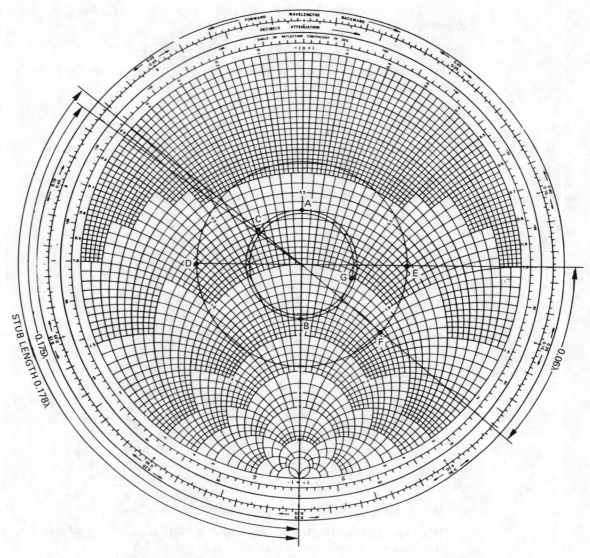

Total admittance at the junction = $Y_{11} + Y_{22} = 2.04 + j0.96$.

Normalising to the 300 $\Omega$ line gives $Y = 1.02 + j0.48$. This is point G on the chart. Draw a circle of radius OG, which gives a V.S.W.R. of 1.6.

Since $Y$ is 1.02 S and may be approximated to 1, the short-circuit stub can be connected at the junction B of the transmission lines to yield a susceptance of j0.48 with a length of 0.178λ to the short-circuit load.

## 6.3 Unworked Problems

### Problem 6.1

At a particular frequency, a line 16 miles long has $Z_0 = 700 \angle -30°$ $\Omega$, an attenuation coefficient of 0.125 Np/mile and a phase change coefficient of 0.06 rad/mile. If the receiving end of the line is short-circuited and the sending-end current is 0.04 $\angle$ 0° A, determine the magnitude and phase angle of (a) the sending-end voltage and (b) the receiving-end short-circuit current.

[(a) 28.6, $\angle -28.7°$ V; (b) 0.011, $\angle -54.7°$ A]

### Problem 6.2

Show, from a consideration of the general equations for the voltage and current on a long transmission line, that the magnitude of the input impedance of a loss-free line of length $\lambda/8$ terminated by any pure resistance is equal to the characteristic impedance of the line.

Hence calculate the resistance required to produce an input impedance having an angle of $+45°$ when connected to a $\lambda/8$ length of loss-free line of characteristic impedance of $100 \angle 0° \ \Omega$.

(IEE Part 3)

[41.4 $\Omega$]

### Problem 6.3

Explain why the velocity of propagation for travelling waves along a transmission line is normally less than that in free space.

A transmission line has a resistance of 15 $\Omega$, negligible leakage, a capacitance of 0.02 $\mu$F and an inductance of 5 mH, all per loop mile. Calculate, for a frequency of 796 Hz, (a) the attenuation and phase change coefficients; (b) the velocity of propagation.

[0.0144 nepers/mile; 0.052 rad/mile; $9 \times 10^4$ miles]

### Problem 6.4

A transmission line has a characteristic impedance $Z_0$ and is terminated with an impedance $Z$. Derive, from the general line equations for voltage and current, an expression for the input impedance of the line in terms of $Z_0$, $Z$ and $Z_{SC}$, where $Z_{SC}$ is the input impedance when the load is short-circuited.

At a particular frequency, $Z_0 = 600 \angle 0° \ \Omega$, $Z = 300 \angle -45° \ \Omega$ and $Z_{SC} = 800 \angle 45° \ \Omega$, and a voltage generator connected to the input of the line has an e.m.f. of 80 V and an internal resistance of 600 $\Omega$. Calculate the current input to the line.

$$\left[ Z_{input} = Z_0^2 \left( \frac{Z + Z_{SC}}{Z_0^2 + ZZ_{SC}} \right) ; \ 73.5 \ \angle -11.25 \ \text{mA} \right]$$

### Problem 6.5

Explain and illustrate the meaning of the terms *travelling wave* and *standing wave* with reference to a uniform transmission line.

A transmission line of surge impedance 75 $\Omega$ is series connected to a second line of surge impedance 400 $\Omega$. A step function of amplitude 10 kV travels along the first line towards the junction. Determine the voltages and currents in the two lines immediately after the surge reaches the junction.

(CEI Part 2)

[16.84 kV; 42.1 A]

### Problem 6.6

An air-spaced loss-free transmission line has a load that produces a voltage reflection coefficient of $0.5 \angle 30°$. The characteristic impedance of the line is $80 \angle 0° \ \Omega$. A generator of internal impedance $80 \angle 0° \ \Omega$ supplies a sinusoidal signal at a frequency of 60 kHz to the line. Determine (a) the impedance of the load; (b) the position of the voltage minimum nearest the load.

[$188 \angle 33.7° \ \Omega$; $0.292\lambda$ or 1.46 km]

## Problem 6.7

The arrangement shown in the diagram is used to provide matching at a single frequency between two loss-free transmission lines with different characteristic impedances $Z_a$ and $Z_b$. The propagation coefficients per unit length are, respec-

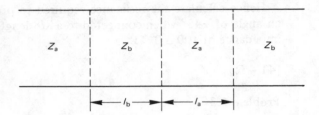

tively, $j\beta_a$ and $j\beta_b$. From consideration of the image impedance of the matching section, show that matching is obtained when

$$\sin \theta = \frac{(k)^{\frac{1}{2}}}{k + 1}$$

where $\theta = \beta_a l_a = \beta_b l_b$; and $k = Z_a/Z_b$.

Comment on the variation of $l_a$ and $l_b$ with $k$, and show that they are always less than $1/12$ of the wavelength.

(CEI Part 2)

## Problem 6.8

Explain why a high value of standing wave ratio is undesirable on a signal transmission line.

A voltage generator, operating at 8 MHz, has an internal source impedance of $(300 + j0)$ $\Omega$. The generator is connected to a load by means of a 600 $\Omega$ loss-free transmission line 7.5 m long. Determine, from the general transmission line equations, the necessary resistance and reactance of the load to absorb maximum power. Take the velocity of propagation on the line to be $3 \times 10^8$ m/s.
[$933 - j410$]

## Problem 6.9

Explain why standing waves on a transmission line can be eliminated by the use of a stub.

A loss-free line of characteristic impedance 400 $\Omega$, terminated in an admittance $Y_t$, transmits a wave of wavelength $\lambda$. The first voltage minimum is $0.05\lambda$ from the termination and the standing wave ratio is 4. Determine (i) $Y_t$; (ii) the position and length (in terms of $\lambda$) of an *open-circuited* stub which maximises the length of the line free of standing waves.

(CEI Part 2)

[(i) $(4.125 - j4.5)$; (ii) $0.024\lambda$, $0.161\lambda$]

## Problem 6.10

A 600 $\Omega$ transmission line supplies a terminating impedance at a frequency of 100 MHz. Measurement discloses a standing wave of ratio 3, with a voltage minimum at 60 cm from the termination. Calculate the effective values of resistive and reactive components of the terminating impedance. Assume that the wavelength on the line is equal to the free space value.

[$1020 - j750 \, \Omega$]

## Problem 6.11

Two dissimilar loss-free transmission lines A and B, each 10 km long, are connected as shown in the diagram. Each line is short-circuited at its far end.

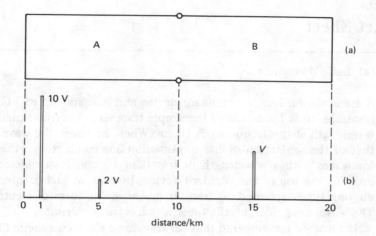

At time $t = 0$, a positive voltage impulse is applied between the conductors at a certain point P in the system. After a time interval too short for a disturbance to reach the far end of either line, the voltage distribution is that in part (b) of the diagram.

    (i) Where was the point P?
   (ii) What was the value of the initial voltage impulse?
  (iii) What is the value of $V$?
  (iv) What can be deduced about the relative properties of the two lines?

(CEI Part 2)

[(i) 8 km in A; (ii) 10 V; (iii) $V = 12$ V; (iv) $Z_b = 1.5 \, Z_a$]

# 7 Waveguides

## 7.1 Fact Sheet

### (a) Basic Waveguide

A transmission line is a standard device and is usable up to 3 GHz, say, when the transmission is by means of the simple transverse electromagnetic wave where the wavelength at this frequency is 10 cm. When, however, the wavelength approaches that of the separation of the transmission line conductors, other waves occur and for waves with a wavelength of less than 10 cm, losses increase rapidly which prohibit the use of the standard device. Instead, at such frequencies, hollow conducting tubes are used to transfer power in the form of electromagnetic waves. The waves are guided by the tube, which is the *waveguide*.

It must be remembered that for transverse electromagnetic (TEM) waves where the electromagnetic field strength vectors are mutually parallel, because of the boundary conditions within the waveguide, such waves cannot propagate along the hollow conducting tube.

The two types of wave which can exist within an enclosed conducting tube are the transverse electric (TE or H) waves and the transverse magnetic (TM or E) waves. In the former, the electric field strength is always transverse to the direction of propagation but the magnetic field strength has both transverse and longitudinal components. For the latter, the magnetic field strength is always transverse to the direction of propagation but the electric field strength has transverse and longitudinal components. Oscillations in the electric field strength of a TE wave are in phase with the tangential magnetic field, which has a phase difference of $\pi/2$ with respect to the longitudinal magnetic field strength. The resultant magnetic field will exhibit elliptical polarisation. The roles of electric and magnetic field are reversed in TM waves.

### (b) Rectangular Waveguide

The procedure for the solution of a waveguide problem is outlined in step form:

1. Start with Maxwell's equations.
2. Apply the restriction of harmonic variation with respect to time.
3. Apply the restriction of harmonic variation and attenuation with respect to distance $z$.
4. Select the type of mode of the wave.
5. Find the equations for the other field components.
6. Develop the scalar wave equation for $\overline{H}_z$.
7. Solve this wave equation for $\overline{H}_z$, subject to the boundary conditions of the waveguide.
8. Substitute $\overline{H}_z$ back into the equations of step 5, which yield a set of equations expressing each field component as a function of space and time.

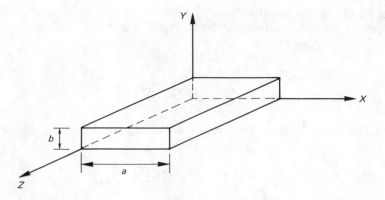

**Fig. 7.1**

A waveguide is shown in Figure 7.1 with $a > b$, with transmission in the $z$ direction. Note that $\gamma^2 = j\omega\mu[\sigma + j\omega\epsilon]$.

The wave equations:

$$\frac{\partial^2 \overline{E}_z}{\partial_x{}^2} + \frac{\partial^2 \overline{E}_z}{\partial_y{}^2} + \frac{\partial^2 \overline{E}_z}{\partial_z{}^2} = -\omega^2 \mu\epsilon \overline{E}_z$$

and

$$\frac{\partial^2 \overline{H}_z}{\partial x^2} + \frac{\partial^2 \overline{H}_z}{\partial y^2} + \frac{\partial^2 \overline{H}_z}{\partial z^2} = -\omega^2 \mu\epsilon \overline{H}_z$$

The solution of these equations is by means of the separation of the variables, so that for the electric field

$$\overline{E}_z = X(x)\, Y(y)\, Z(z)$$

where $X(x)$, $Y(y)$, $Z(z)$ are functions of $x$, $y$ and $z$ only. The boundary conditions are

$$E_t = 0 \text{ at } x = 0, x = a$$

$$E_t = 0 \text{ at } y = 0, y = b$$

so that suitable functions for the $X(x)$ and $Y(y)$ functions are trigonometrical and of the form $\sin(m\pi x/a)$ and $\sin(n\pi y/b)$, respectively. Here $m$ and $n$ are integers or zero. The solution is

$$\overline{E}_z = E_0 \sin\left(\frac{m\pi x}{a}\right) \sin\left(\frac{n\pi y}{b}\right) e^{j(\omega t - \beta z)}$$

Assuming propagation is without attenuation, consider the equation

$$\operatorname{curl} \overline{E} = -\mu_0 \frac{\partial \overline{H}}{\partial t}$$

Substituting $\partial/\partial_z = -j\beta$ yields

$$\frac{\partial \overline{E}_z}{\partial y} + j\beta \overline{E}_y = -j\omega\mu \overline{H}_x$$

$$-\partial\beta \overline{E}_x + \frac{\partial \overline{E}_z}{\partial x} = -j\omega\mu \overline{H}_y$$

$$\frac{\partial \overline{E}_y}{\partial x} - \frac{\partial \overline{E}_x}{\partial y} = -j\omega\mu \overline{H}_z$$

Hence, the expressions for the $x$- and $y$-directed components in terms of the $z$-directed components derivatives may be arranged to give

$$\beta \overline{E}_x - \omega\mu\overline{H}_y = j\,\frac{\partial \overline{E}_x}{\partial x}$$

$$\beta \overline{E}_y + \omega\mu\overline{H}_z = j\,\frac{\partial \overline{E}_z}{\partial y}$$

Repeating this procedure for the curl $\overline{H}$ equation, the following equations are developed:

$$\omega\epsilon\overline{E}_x - \beta\overline{H}_y = j\,\frac{\partial \overline{H}_z}{\partial y}$$

$$\omega\epsilon\overline{E}_y + \beta\overline{H}_x = j\,\frac{\partial \overline{H}_z}{\partial x}$$

These may be rewritten to yield

$$\overline{E}_x = \frac{-j}{\omega^2\mu\epsilon - \beta^2}\left[\beta\,\frac{\partial \overline{E}_z}{\partial x} + \omega\mu\,\frac{\partial \overline{H}_z}{\partial y}\right]$$

$$\overline{E}_y = \frac{j}{\omega^2\mu\epsilon - \beta^2}\left[-\beta\,\frac{\partial \overline{E}_z}{\partial y} + \omega\mu\,\frac{\partial \overline{H}_z}{\partial x}\right]$$

$$\overline{H}_x = \frac{j}{\omega^2\mu\epsilon - \beta^2}\left[\omega\epsilon\,\frac{\partial \overline{E}_z}{\partial y} - \beta\,\frac{\partial \overline{H}_z}{\partial x}\right]$$

$$\overline{H}_y = \frac{-j}{\omega^2\mu\epsilon - \beta^2}\left[\omega\epsilon\,\frac{\partial \overline{E}_z}{\partial x} + \beta\,\frac{\partial \overline{H}_z}{\partial y}\right]$$

In these equations $\overline{H}_z$ and $\overline{E}_z$ are independent variables and two types of solution are possible — namely those for which $\overline{E}_z = 0$ and those for which $\overline{H}_z = 0$, thus producing solutions for TE and TM modes.

## (c) Transverse Electric TE Mode

In this case $\overline{E}_z = 0$ and if $\overline{E}_y = 0$ at $x = 0$ and $x = a$ and $\overline{E}_x = 0$ at $y = 0$ and $y = b$, hence $\partial \overline{H}_z/\partial t = 0$. The solution for the magnetic field variation is

$$\overline{H}_z = H_0\,\cos\left(\frac{m\pi x}{a}\right)\,\cos\left(\frac{n\pi y}{b}\right)\,e^{j(\omega t - \beta z)}$$

and using this with the previous equations gives

$$\overline{H}_x = \frac{H_0 j\,\beta\,m\,\pi}{(\omega^2\mu\epsilon - \beta^2)a}\,\sin\left(\frac{m\pi x}{a}\right)\,\cos\left(\frac{n\pi y}{b}\right)\,e^{j(\omega t - \beta z)}$$

$$\overline{H}_y = \frac{H_0 j\beta}{(\omega^2\mu\epsilon - \beta^2)}\,\frac{n\pi}{b}\,\cos\left(\frac{m\pi x}{a}\right)\,\sin\left(\frac{n\pi y}{b}\right)\,e^{j(\omega t - \beta z)}$$

$$\overline{E}_x = \frac{j\omega\mu H_0}{(\omega^2\mu\epsilon - \beta^2)}\,\frac{n\pi}{b}\,\cos\left(\frac{m\pi x}{a}\right)\,\sin\left(\frac{n\pi y}{b}\right)\,e^{j(\omega t - \beta z)}$$

$$\overline{E}_y = \frac{(-j\omega\mu)\,H_0}{(\omega^2\mu\epsilon - \beta^2)}\,\frac{m\pi}{a}\,\sin\left(\frac{m\pi x}{a}\right)\,\cos\left(\frac{n\pi y}{b}\right)\,e^{j(\omega t - \beta z)}$$

For the $TE_{10}$ mode, the dominant mode in rectangular waveguides, $m = 1$, $n = 0$ and the cut-off wavelength $\lambda_c = 2a$. Also

$$\omega^2 \mu \epsilon - \beta^2 = \left(\frac{m\pi}{a}\right)^2 + \left(\frac{n\pi}{b}\right)^2$$

$$\text{velocity of light } c = \frac{1}{(\mu\epsilon)^{\frac{1}{2}}}$$

so for an air-filled waveguide

$$\beta = \left[\frac{\omega^2}{c^2} - \left(\frac{m\pi}{a}\right)^2 - \left(\frac{n\pi}{b}\right)^2\right]^{\frac{1}{2}}$$

For the $TE_{10}$ mode

$$\beta = \left(\frac{\omega^2}{c^2} - \frac{\pi^2}{a^2}\right)^{\frac{1}{2}}$$

Hence,

$$\text{frequency of cut-off } f_c = \frac{c}{2\pi}\left[\left(\frac{m\pi}{a}\right)^2 + \left(\frac{n\pi}{b}\right)^2\right]^{\frac{1}{2}}$$

for the $TE_{10}$ mode

$$f_c = \frac{c}{2\pi}\left(\frac{\pi^2}{a^2}\right)^{\frac{1}{2}} = \frac{c}{2a}$$

$$\text{wavelength in the guide } \lambda_g = \frac{\lambda}{[\epsilon_r - (\lambda/\lambda_c)^2]^{\frac{1}{2}}}$$

where $\epsilon_r$ is the relative permittivity of the dielectric filling the interior of the guide (for air $\epsilon_r = 1$), while $\lambda$ is the free-space wavelength.

$$\text{phase velocity} = \frac{\omega}{\beta}$$

## (d) Transverse Magnetic TM Mode

The propagation equations are

$$\overline{H}_x = \frac{j\omega\epsilon E_0}{\omega^2 \mu\epsilon - \beta^2} \frac{n\pi}{b} \sin\left(\frac{m\pi x}{a}\right) \cos\left(\frac{n\pi y}{b}\right) e^{-j(\omega t - \beta z)}$$

$$\overline{H}_y = \frac{-j\omega\epsilon E_0}{\omega^2 \mu\epsilon - \beta^2} \frac{m\pi}{a} \sin\left(\frac{m\pi x}{a}\right) \sin\left(\frac{n\pi y}{b}\right) e^{j(\omega t - \beta z)}$$

$$\overline{E}_x = \frac{-jE_0\beta}{\omega^2 \mu\epsilon - \beta^2} \frac{m\pi}{a} \cos\left(\frac{m\pi x}{a}\right) \sin\left(\frac{n\pi y}{b}\right) e^{j(\omega t - \beta z)}$$

$$\overline{E}_y = \frac{-jE_0\beta}{\omega^2 \mu\epsilon - \beta^2} \frac{n\pi}{b} \sin\left(\frac{m\pi x}{a}\right) \cos\left(\frac{n\pi y}{b}\right) e^{j(\omega t - \beta z)}$$

$$\overline{E}_z = E_0 \sin\left(\frac{m\pi x}{a}\right) \sin\left(\frac{n\pi y}{b}\right) e^{j(\omega t - \beta z)}$$

The equations for the phase coefficient, for the cut-off frequency and for the various wavelengths are similar to those for the TE mode.

It should be noted that $m$ is an indication of the number of field variations in the $x$ direction, while $n$ indicates the number of field variations with the $y$ direction; thus, $TM_{11}$ mode means $m = 1$, $n = 1$, while $TE_{10}$ mode means $m = 1$, $n = 0$.

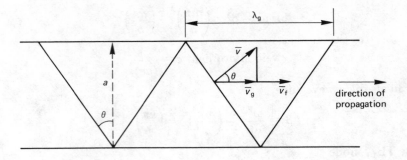

**Fig. 7.2**

In Figure 7.2 various wave fronts are shown where $\theta$ is the angle that the component wave fronts make with the walls of the guide:

$$\lambda_g \text{ (wavelength of the guide)} = 2a \tan \theta$$

also

$$\overline{v}_g = v \cos \theta$$

from the vector diagram in Figure 7.2, where $\overline{v}$ is the velocity of the component waves and $\overline{v}_g$ is the group velocity.

$$\overline{v}_f = \text{the phase velocity} = \frac{\overline{v}}{\cos \theta}$$

so that

$$\overline{v}_g \times \overline{v}_f = \overline{v} \cos \theta \times \frac{\overline{v}}{\cos \theta} = \overline{v}^2 = c^2$$

$c$ is velocity of air in the tube medium.

### (e) Power Flow in a Rectangular Waveguide

From Poynting's vector equation, one may obtain the power flowing along a waveguide. But this equation must be applied over a surface which encloses a volume. The only contribution to the integral is from within the waveguide.

$$\text{Power } \overline{P} = \tfrac{1}{2} \int \text{Re} \cdot \overline{E} \times \overline{H}^* \cdot ds$$
$$\text{waveguide}$$
$$\text{cross-section}$$

For the dominant TE mode, where $m = 1$ and $n = 0$,

$$E_0 = \frac{-j\omega\mu_0}{\omega^2 \mu\epsilon - \beta^2} \cdot \frac{\pi}{a} \cdot H_0$$

so that

$$\overline{E}_y = E_0 \sin\left(\frac{\pi x}{a}\right) e^{-j\beta z}$$

and

$$\overline{H}_x = \frac{-\beta}{\omega\mu} E_0 \sin\left(\frac{\pi x}{a}\right) e^{-j\beta z}$$

$$\text{Power density } p = \tfrac{1}{2} \frac{E^2_{\max}}{Z_{\text{TE}}} \sin^2\left(\frac{\pi x}{a}\right)$$

160

since the maximum power which can be transmitted along the waveguide is determined by the maximum electric field intensity.

$Z_{TE} = \dfrac{\omega\mu}{\beta}$ is the wave impedance of TE modes.

$E_{max}$ is the modulus of $\overline{E}$.

The total power transmitted is

$$\overline{P} = \int\limits_{\substack{\text{waveguide}\\ \text{cross-section}}} p \cdot dx \cdot dy = \frac{1}{2}\frac{E_{max}^{\,2}}{Z_{TE}}\int_0^b\int_0^a \sin^2\left(\frac{\pi x}{a}\right)dx \cdot dy$$

and evaluating the integrals yields

$$\overline{P} = \frac{E_{max}^{\,2}\,ab}{4Z_{TE}}$$

As $E_{max}$ is constant in this equation, the power transmitted is determined by the cross-sectional area $ab$, of the waveguide.

### (f) Attenuation

The propagation along a waveguide has been described by the factor $e^{-j\beta z}$. Above the cut-off frequency, the phase change coefficient is real. Below the cut-off frequency it is known that $\beta$ is imaginary, which describes an attenuated wave that is not propagating. It is referred to as an *evanescent* wave. These results, for a waveguide, assume infinitely conducting walls and a perfect dielectric filling.

In practice the waveguide is constructed of a good but not perfect conducting material and the dielectric may be lossy. Both these conditions reduce the magnitude of the wave as it propagates. That is, there is attenuation, so that $\beta$ has a small imaginary component.

## 7.2 Worked Examples

### Example 7.1

A waveguide consists of two extensive and perfectly conducting flat sheets set parallel and 0.1 m apart in air. For how many $TE_{on}$ modes is unattenuated propagation possible at a frequency of 5 GHz, and what are the velocities of propagation in these modes?

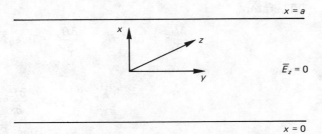

The diagram shows the general arrangements of the waveguide, assuming the fields are independent of $y$ but vary with time $t$ and distance $z$, in the form $e^{(j\omega t - \gamma z)}$.

(Leeds Polytechnic)

### Solution 7.1

(1) Consider $\bar{E}$ has an $\bar{E}_x$ component only. Maxwell's curl equations are

$$\begin{vmatrix} u_x & u_y & u_z \\ \partial/\partial x & \partial/\partial y & \partial/\partial z \\ \bar{E}_x & 0 & 0 \end{vmatrix} = -j\omega\mu_0\bar{H}$$

Therefore,

$$\bar{H}_x = 0, \quad \bar{H}_y = \frac{+\gamma}{j\omega\mu_0} \cdot \bar{E}_x \text{ and } \bar{H}_z = 0$$

Then

$$\begin{vmatrix} u_x & u_y & u_z \\ \partial/\partial x & \partial/\partial y & \partial/\partial z \\ 0 & \bar{H}_y & 0 \end{vmatrix} = +j\omega\epsilon_0\bar{E}$$

Therefore,

$$\bar{H}_y = \frac{+j\omega\epsilon_0\bar{E}_x}{\gamma}, \quad \bar{E}_y = 0, \quad \bar{E}_z = 0$$

For TEM mode propagation ($y = \infty$) and fields $\bar{E}_x$ and $\bar{H}_y$ only,

$$\gamma^2 = (j\omega)^2 \mu_0\epsilon_0; \quad \gamma = \alpha + j\beta$$

Therefore,

$$\beta = \omega(\mu_0\epsilon_0)^{\frac{1}{2}} \text{ and } \frac{\omega}{\beta} = \text{velocity}$$

(2) Consider $\bar{E}$ has an $\bar{E}_y$ component only; then

$$\begin{vmatrix} u_x & u_y & u_z \\ \partial/\partial x & \partial/\partial y & \partial/\partial z \\ 0 & \bar{E}_y & 0 \end{vmatrix} = -j\omega\mu_0\bar{H}$$

Therefore,

$$-j\omega\mu_0 \bar{H}_x = \gamma\bar{E}_y, \quad \bar{H}_y = 0 \text{ and } +j\omega\mu_0\bar{H}_z = \frac{-\partial \bar{E}_y}{\partial x}$$

Hence,

$$\begin{vmatrix} u_x & u_y & u_z \\ \partial/\partial x & \partial/\partial y & \partial/\partial z \\ \bar{H}_x & 0 & \bar{H}_z \end{vmatrix} = +j\omega\epsilon_0\bar{E}$$

Therefore,

$$\frac{\partial \bar{H}_z}{\partial y} = 0; \quad -\bar{H}_x - \frac{\partial \bar{H}_z}{\partial x} = j\omega\epsilon_0\bar{E}_y; \quad \frac{\partial \bar{H}_x}{\partial y} = 0$$

Now

$$\frac{\partial^2 \bar{E}_y}{\partial x^2} = -j\omega\mu_0 \frac{\partial \bar{H}_z}{\partial x}$$

$$= j\omega\mu_0 [j\omega\epsilon_0\bar{E}_y + \bar{H}_x]$$

$$= (j\omega)^2 \mu_0\epsilon_0\bar{E}_y - \gamma^2 \bar{E}_y$$

$$\frac{\partial^2 \bar{E}_y}{\partial x^2} + k^2 \bar{E}_y = 0$$

where

$$k^2 = \omega^2 \mu_0 \epsilon_0 + \gamma^2$$

The solution for this differential equation is of the form

$$\overline{E}_y = A \cos kx + B \sin kx$$

but $\overline{E}_y = 0$ at $x = 0$ and $x = a$ boundary conditions, so $A = 0$ and $ka = n\pi$, $n \neq 0$.
Now for non-attenuating mode $\gamma = j\beta$; therefore,

$$\beta^2 = \omega^2 \mu_0 \epsilon_0 - k^2 = \omega^2 \mu_0 \epsilon_0 - \left(\frac{n\pi}{a}\right)^2$$

For $\beta$ to be real, $\omega^2 \mu_0 \epsilon_0 > \left(\frac{n\pi}{a}\right)^2$ — that is,

$$\frac{\omega}{c} > \frac{n\pi}{a} \text{ or } n < \frac{2af}{c}$$

where $c$ is velocity of propagation and $f$ the frequency.
Numerical solution for $f = 5$ GHz, $a = 0.1$ m and $c = 3 \times 10^8$ m/s. Therefore,

$$n < \frac{2 \times 0.1 \times 5 \times 10^9}{3 \times 10^8} < \frac{10}{3}$$

This means that the only propagating modes are TEM, $TE_{01}$, $TE_{02}$, $TE_{03}$.
The phase velocity $v_p = \omega/\beta$ or

$$v_p = \frac{\omega}{\left[\left(\frac{\omega}{c}\right)^2 - \left(\frac{n\pi}{a}\right)^2\right]^{\frac{1}{2}}} = \frac{c}{\left[1 - \left(\frac{nc}{2fa}\right)^2\right]^{\frac{1}{2}}}$$

$$TE_{01} \qquad v_p = 3.14 \times 10^8 \text{ m/s}$$
$$TE_{02} \qquad v_p = 3.75 \times 10^8 \text{ m/s}$$
$$TE_{03} \qquad v_p = 6.88 \times 10^8 \text{ m/s}$$

**Example 7.2**

A waveguide with rectangular cross-section has dimensions 20 mm high by 40 mm wide. Assuming TE operation, good conductivity of the walls, and the dielectric to be air, calculate (a) the mode, (b) the guide wavelength, (c) the phase velocity and (d) the group velocity, if the guide is operating at a frequency 20 per cent higher than the cut-off level.

*Solution 7.2*

For a $TE_{10}$ mode, $m = 1$, $n = 0$.

(a) $\lambda_c = \dfrac{2}{\left[\left(\frac{1}{a}\right)^2\right]^{\frac{1}{2}}} = 2a = 0.08$ m $= 80$ mm

Thus,

$$f_c = \frac{3 \times 10^8}{0.08} = 3750 \text{ MHz}$$

Twenty per cent above this value is 4500 MHz; therefore,

$$\lambda = \frac{3 \times 10^8}{4.5 \times 10^9} = 0.067 \text{ m}$$

For the $TE_{11}$ mode, $m = 1$, $n = 1$.

$$\lambda_c = \frac{2}{\left[ \left( \frac{1}{b} \right)^2 \right]^{\frac{1}{2}}} = 2b = 0.04 \text{ m}$$

$f_c = 7500$ MHz, so the performance must be restricted to the $TE_{10}$ mode, as the increase in the frequency is over 20 per cent.

(b) Guide wavelength $\lambda_g = \dfrac{\lambda}{[1 - (\lambda/\lambda_c)^2]^{\frac{1}{2}}}$

$$\lambda_g = \frac{0.067}{\left[ 1 - \left( \frac{0.067}{0.08} \right)^2 \right]^{\frac{1}{2}}} = 0.123 \text{ m}$$

(c) As $\theta$ is the angle the component wave makes with the guide wall,

$$\lambda_g = 2a \tan \theta$$

or

$$\tan \theta = \frac{0.123}{2 \times 0.04} = 1.5375$$

$$\theta = 57°$$

Thus,

$$\text{phase velocity } \overline{v}_f = \frac{3 \times 10^8}{0.545} = 5.5 \times 10^8 \text{ m/s}$$

(d) $\quad\quad\quad \text{Group velocity } \overline{v}_g = \dfrac{c^2}{v_f} = \dfrac{9 \times 10^{16}}{5.5 \times 10^8} = 1.64 \times 10^8 \text{ m/s}$

## Example 7.3

Assume a parallel plane waveguide consisting of two sheets of good conductor separated by 0.1 m and operated in the $TE_{10}$ mode. Find the propagation coefficient $\gamma$ at frequencies of 100 MHz, 1000 MHz and 10 GHz. Does propagation take place?

Repeat the question if the guide is excited in the $TE_{20}$ mode.

## Solution 7.3

(a) $m = 1$, $n = 0$.

$$\gamma = \left[ \left( \frac{\pi}{a} \right)^2 - 4\pi^2 f^2 \mu_0 \epsilon_0 \right]^{\frac{1}{2}}$$

$$= \pi \left[ \left( \frac{1}{a} \right)^2 - \left( \frac{2f}{c} \right)^2 \right]^{\frac{1}{2}}$$

(i) At 100 MHz:

$$\gamma = \pi \left[ \left( \frac{1}{0.1} \right)^2 - \left( \frac{200 \times 10^6}{3 \times 10^8} \right)^2 \right]^{\frac{1}{2}}$$

$$= 31.35 \text{ nepers/m}$$

As $\gamma$ is real, there is *no propagation*.

(ii) At 1000 MHz:

$$\gamma = \pi \left[ 100 - \left( \frac{20 \times 10^8}{3 \times 10^8} \right)^2 \right]^{\frac{1}{2}} = \underline{23.42 \text{ nepers/m}}$$

Again, as in case (i), $\gamma$ is real, so there is *no propagation*.

(iii) At 10 GHz:

$$\gamma = \pi \left[ 100 - \left( \frac{200}{3} \right)^2 \right]^{\frac{1}{2}} = \underline{j\ 207 \text{ rad/m}}$$

Here $\gamma$ is imaginary, so $\beta = 207$ rad/m and *propagation takes place*.

(b) $m = 2$, $n = 0$.

$$\gamma = \left[ \left( \frac{2\pi}{a} \right)^2 - 4\pi^2 f^2 \mu_0 \epsilon_0 \right]^{\frac{1}{2}} = 2\pi \left[ \left( \frac{1}{a} \right)^2 - \left( \frac{f}{c} \right)^2 \right]^{\frac{1}{2}}$$

(i) $\qquad \gamma = 2\pi \left[ \left( \frac{1}{0.1} \right)^2 - \left( \frac{10^8}{3 \times 10^8} \right)^2 \right]^{\frac{1}{2}} = \underline{62.8 \text{ nepers/m}}$

Here $\gamma$ is real; therefore, there is *no propagation*.

(ii) $\qquad \gamma = 2\pi \left[ 100 - \left( \frac{10^9}{3 \times 10^8} \right)^2 \right]^{\frac{1}{2}} = \underline{59.24 \text{ nepers/m}}$

This is still below cut-off; therefore, there is no propagation.

(iii) $\qquad \gamma = 2\pi \left[ 100 - \left( \frac{10^{10}}{3 \times 10^8} \right)^2 \right]^{\frac{1}{2}} = \underline{j\ 200}$

*Propagation does take place*, as $\gamma$ is imaginary, so $\beta = 200$ rad/m.

### Example 7.4

The propagation mode in an air-filled rectangular waveguide (see diagram) is such that the amplitudes are

$$\bar{E}_z = 0; \quad \bar{H}_z = A e^{-\gamma z} \cos \frac{\pi}{b} y$$

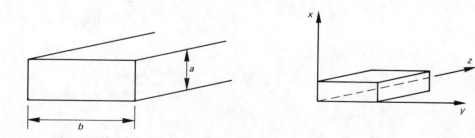

Show that for propagation to be possible without attenuation, the angular frequency must be $\omega > \omega_0$, when $\omega_0^2 = \left( \frac{\pi}{b} \right)^2 \times \frac{1}{\mu_0 \epsilon_0}$ .

Derive the other components of $\bar{E}$ and $\bar{H}$ and sketch the field pattern in the guide.

### Solution 7.4

Assume time variations to be of the form $e^{j\omega t}$. Maxwell's curl equations give

$$\begin{vmatrix} u_x & u_y & u_z \\ \partial/\partial x & \partial/\partial y & \partial/\partial z \\ \overline{E}_x & \overline{E}_y & 0 \end{vmatrix} = -j\omega\mu_0\overline{H}$$

$$\begin{vmatrix} u_x & u_y & u_z \\ \partial/\partial x & \partial/\partial y & \partial/\partial z \\ \overline{H}_x & \overline{H}_y & \overline{H}_z \end{vmatrix} = j\omega\epsilon_0\overline{E}$$

Assume all the $z$ variations to be of the form $e^{-\gamma z}$, so that

$$\overline{E}_x = Be^{-\gamma z}; \overline{E}_y = Ce^{-\gamma z}; \overline{H}_x = De^{-\gamma z}; \overline{H}_y = Fe^{-\gamma z}$$

Then

$$\gamma C = -j\omega\mu_0 D$$

$$\gamma B = j\omega\mu_0 F$$

$$\frac{\partial C}{\partial x} - \frac{\partial B}{\partial y} = -j\omega\mu_0 A \cos\frac{\pi y}{b}$$

Similarly,

$$\frac{-\pi A}{b} \sin\frac{\pi y}{b} + \gamma F = j\omega\epsilon_0 B$$

Thus,

$$-\gamma D = j\omega\epsilon_0 C$$

$$\frac{\partial F}{\partial x} - \frac{\partial D}{\partial y} = 0$$

From the above,

$$\frac{C}{D} = \frac{-j\omega\mu_0}{\gamma} = -\frac{\gamma}{j\omega\epsilon_0}$$

Thus,

$$\gamma^2 = (j\omega)^2 \mu_0\epsilon_0$$

so $C = D = 0$. This is what one would expect from the initial equations. Also

$$\frac{-\gamma\pi A}{b} \sin\frac{\pi y}{b} + \gamma^2 F = j\omega\epsilon_0 \times j\omega\mu_0 F$$

Thus,

$$F = \frac{\gamma A\pi \sin(\pi y/b)}{b(\gamma^2 + \omega^2\mu_0\epsilon_0)}$$

and

$$B = \frac{j\omega\mu_0 \pi A \sin(\pi y/b)}{b(\gamma^2 + \omega^2\mu_0\epsilon_0)}$$

If $C$ and $D \neq 0$ or $\gamma^2 + \omega^2\mu_0\epsilon_0 = 0$, then $F = B = \infty$; hence, $C = D = 0$. Hence,

$$\frac{j\omega\epsilon_0 A\pi^2}{b^2(\gamma^2 + \omega^2\mu_0\epsilon_0)} = j\omega\mu_0 A$$

Thus,

$$\gamma^2 + \omega^2 \mu_0 \epsilon_0 = \left(\frac{\pi}{b}\right)^2$$

For propagation without attenuation, $\gamma = j\beta$, $\beta$ real — that is,

$$\beta^2 = \omega^2 \mu_0 \epsilon_0 - \left(\frac{\pi}{b}\right)^2$$

or $\beta^2 > 0$, so that

$$\omega^2 > \frac{\pi^2}{b^2} \times \frac{1}{\mu_0 \epsilon_0} = \omega_0^2 \quad \text{(say)}$$

Thus,

$$\overline{E}_x = \frac{j\omega\mu_0 bA}{\pi} \sin \frac{\pi y}{b} e^{-j\beta z}$$

$$\overline{H}_y = \frac{j\beta bA}{\pi} \sin \frac{\pi y}{b} e^{-j\beta z}$$

These equations satisfy the boundary conditions at $y = 0$ and $y = b$. The field patterns are shown in the diagram.

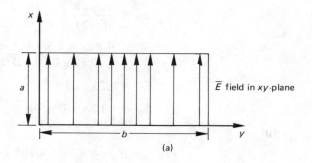

$\overline{E}$ field in $xy$-plane

(a)

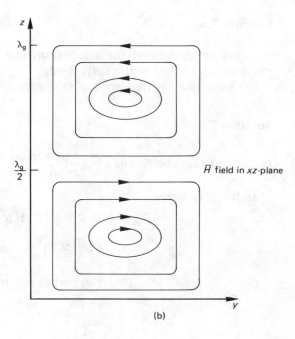

$\overline{H}$ field in $xz$-plane

(b)

## Example 7.5

A rectangular guide has dimensions $a = 30$ mm and $b = 20$ mm through which 5 kW is transmitted at 7.5 GHz. Calculate the characteristic impedance and the maximum voltage across the 20 mm dimension of the guide.

### Solution 7.5

Assume that the guide is in the $TE_{10}$ mode.

$$Z_0 = \frac{\omega \mu_0}{\beta} \cdot \frac{2b}{a}$$

$$= \frac{2\pi \times 7.5 \times 10^9}{157} \times \frac{4\pi}{10^7} \times \frac{4}{3} = \underline{503 \ \Omega}$$

since $\beta$ is calculated from

$$\beta = \left[ \frac{\omega^2}{c^2} - \left( \frac{\pi}{a} \right)^2 \right]^{\frac{1}{2}} = \left[ \frac{4\pi^2 \times 7.5^2 \times 10^{18}}{9 \times 10^{16}} - \left( \frac{\pi}{3} \right)^2 \right]^{\frac{1}{2}}$$

$$\beta = 157 \ \text{rad/m}$$

Now

$$E_0^2 = \frac{4\omega \mu_0 W}{\beta (ab)}$$

$$= \frac{4 \times 2\pi \times 7.5 \times 10^9 \times 4\pi \times 5000}{157 \times 0.03 \times 0.02 \times 10^7}$$

$$= 1.257 \times 10^{10}$$

$$E_0 = 1.12 \times 10^5 \ \text{V/m}$$

But

$$V_{\text{max}} = E_0 \times b = 1.12 \times 10^5 \times 0.02 = \underline{2242 \ \text{V}}$$

## Example 7.6

(a) Find an expression for attenuation due to conductor losses between two planes, when excited in the $TM_{10}$ mode.

(b) Show that the frequency of minimum attenuation is $\sqrt{3} \cdot f_c$.

### Solution 7.6

(a) Attenuation coefficient $\alpha = \dfrac{\text{power absorbed}}{2 \times \text{power transmitted}}$

In the $TM_1$ mode,

$$P_{\text{ab}} = \tfrac{1}{2} J_z^2 R = \tfrac{1}{2} |\bar{H}_y|^2 R$$

$$= \tfrac{1}{2} E_0^2 \left( \frac{\omega \mu_0}{2\sigma} \right)^{\frac{1}{2}} \text{ per plate}$$

$$P_{\text{trans}} = \tfrac{1}{2} \text{ real part of } \bar{E} \times \bar{H}^* = \tfrac{1}{2} \bar{E}_x \cdot \bar{H}_y$$

$$= \frac{E_0^2 \ \beta}{2\omega \epsilon_0} \cos^2 \frac{m\pi x}{a}$$

$$\text{Total power transmitted} = \frac{E_0{}^2 \beta}{2\omega\epsilon_0} \int_0^b \int_0^a \cos^2\left(\frac{m\pi x}{a}\right) dx\ dy$$

$$\text{Total } P_{\text{trans}} = \frac{E_0^2 \beta ab}{4\omega\epsilon_0} \ (m = 1)$$

while

$$\text{total } P_{\text{ab}} = 2 \times \tfrac{1}{2} E_0{}^2 \left(\frac{\omega\mu_0}{2\sigma}\right)^{\frac{1}{2}}$$

for both plates. Therefore,

$$\alpha = \frac{E_0{}^2 \left(\dfrac{\omega\mu_0}{2\sigma}\right)^{\frac{1}{2}}}{2E_0{}^2 \dfrac{\beta ab}{4\omega\epsilon_0}} = \frac{(\omega\mu_0/2\sigma)^{\frac{1}{2}}}{\beta ab/2\omega\epsilon_0}$$

But

$$\beta = [\omega^2 \mu_0 \epsilon_0 - \omega_c{}^2 \mu_0 \epsilon_0]^{\frac{1}{2}} = [\mu_0 \epsilon_0]^{\frac{1}{2}} [\omega^2 - \omega_c{}^2]^{\frac{1}{2}}$$

on substituting for $\beta$ in the equation for $\alpha$.

$$\alpha = \frac{(\omega\mu_0/2\sigma)^{\frac{1}{2}} \cdot 2\omega\epsilon_0}{ab \cdot [\mu_0 \epsilon_0]^{\frac{1}{2}} [\omega^2 - \omega_c{}^2]^{\frac{1}{2}}}$$

$$\alpha = \frac{1}{ab} \left[\frac{2\epsilon_0}{\sigma}\right]^{\frac{1}{2}} \left[\frac{\omega^{\frac{3}{2}}}{(\omega^2 - \omega_c{}^2)^{\frac{1}{2}}}\right]$$

(b) To find the minimum value, evaluate $d\alpha/d\omega$ and equate to zero.

$$\frac{d\alpha}{d\omega} = K\left[(\omega^2 - \omega_c{}^2)^{-\frac{1}{2}} \tfrac{3}{2} \omega^{\frac{1}{2}} - \omega^{\frac{3}{2}} \tfrac{1}{2} (\omega^2 - \omega_c{}^2)^{-\frac{3}{2}} 2\omega\right]$$

$$= \frac{\tfrac{3}{2} \omega^{\frac{1}{2}}}{(\omega^2 - \omega_c{}^2)^{\frac{1}{2}}} - \frac{\omega^{\frac{5}{2}}}{(\omega^2 - \omega_c{}^2)^{\frac{3}{2}}} = 0$$

Thus,

$$\tfrac{3}{2} (\omega^2 - \omega_c{}^2)^{\frac{3}{2}} = \omega^2 (\omega^2 - \omega_c{}^2)^{\frac{1}{2}}$$

$$\omega^2 = \tfrac{3}{2} (\omega^2 - \omega_c{}^2)$$

$$\omega^2 = 3\omega_c{}^2 \text{ or } \omega = \sqrt{3}\ \omega_c$$

Therefore,

$$f_{\min} = \sqrt{3} \cdot f_c$$

## Example 7.7

Show that the magnetic field strength in a flat sheet of large surface area is given by

$$\frac{\partial^2 \bar{H}}{\partial y^2} = \sigma\mu \frac{\partial \bar{H}}{\partial t}$$

if the applied field is uniform and parallel to the surface.

Show that the eddy current in such a sheet will reduce the alternating magnetic field at the centre so that the ratio between the magnitudes of surface and central field is given by

$$\left|\frac{H_s}{H_c}\right|^2 = \tfrac{1}{2}\left[\cosh\frac{2a}{\delta} + \cos\frac{2a}{\delta}\right]$$

where $2a$ is the thickness of the sheet, $\delta = \left[\dfrac{2}{\sigma\mu\omega}\right]^{\frac{1}{2}}$ is the depth of penetration and $\omega$ is the angular frequency of the magnetic field ($e^{j\omega t}$).

### Solution 7.7

From Maxwell's first two equations,

$$\nabla \times \bar{H} = \bar{J} = \sigma\bar{E}$$

$$\nabla \times \bar{E} = -\frac{\partial \bar{B}}{\partial t} = -\mu\frac{\partial \bar{H}}{\partial t}$$

and

$$\nabla \times \nabla \times \bar{H} = \sigma \times \nabla \times \bar{E} = -\sigma\mu\frac{\partial \bar{H}}{\partial t}$$

Assume that the magnetic field operates in the $y$ direction; therefore,

$$\frac{\partial^2 \bar{H}}{\partial y^2} = \sigma\mu\frac{\partial \bar{H}}{\partial t}$$

which, for an exponential time-dependent signal $e^{j\omega t}$, reduces to

$$\frac{d^2 \bar{H}}{dy^2} = j\omega\sigma\mu\bar{H}$$

The solution to this type of equation which has exponential time dependence is

$$\bar{H} = A e^{(1+j)y/\delta} + B e^{-(1+j)y/\delta}$$

where

$$\delta = \left[\frac{2}{\omega\mu\sigma}\right]^{\frac{1}{2}} = \left[\frac{1}{\pi f\mu\sigma}\right]^{\frac{1}{2}}$$

Let $\bar{H}_s$ be the surface value of $\bar{H}$ — that is, at $y = 0$, $y = 2a$; therefore,

$$\bar{H}_s = A + B$$

or

$$\bar{H}_s = A e^{(1+j)2s} + B e^{-(1+j)2s}$$

letting $s = a/\delta$. Hence,

$$A e^{(1+j)s}[e^{(1+j)s} - e^{-(1+j)s}] = B e^{-(1+j)s}[e^{(1+j)s} - e^{-(1+j)s}]$$

$$B = A e^{(1+j)2s}$$

Hence,

$$\bar{H}_s = A[1 + e^{(1+j)2s}]$$

Thus,

$$A = \frac{\bar{H}_s}{1 + e^{(1+j)2s}}$$

$$\bar{H} = \frac{\bar{H}_s}{1 + e^{(1+j)2s}}[e^{(1+j)y/\delta} + e^{(1+j)2s}e^{-(1+j)y/\delta}]$$

When $y = a$,

$$\bar{H}_0 = \frac{\bar{H}_s}{1 + e^{(1+j)2s}} \left[ e^{(1+j)s} + e^{(1+j)s} \right]$$

$$= \frac{\bar{H}_s}{\cosh (s + js)}$$

The ratio $\bar{H}_s/\bar{H}_0$ becomes $\cosh (s + js)$ or

$$\cosh (s + js) = \cosh s \cos s + j \sinh s \sin s$$

Therefore,

$$\frac{|H_s|^2}{|H_0|} = \cosh^2 s \cos^2 s + \sinh^2 s \sin^2 s$$

$$= \tfrac{1}{2} \left[ \cosh 2s + \cos 2s \right]$$

**Example 7.8**

Derive an expression for the attenuation of TE waves in a waveguide consisting of two parallel conducting plates separated by a distance $a$.

*Solution 7.8*

It is known that the magnitude of current density is equal to the tangential component of the field intensity at the surface of both plates — that is, $\bar{H}_z$ at $x = 0$ and $x = a$. Thus, $|J_x| = |H_z|$.

The magnitude of $\bar{H}_z$ is

$$\bar{H}_z = \frac{-m\pi E_0}{j\omega\mu_0 a}$$

or

$$|H_z| = \frac{m\pi E_0}{\omega\mu_0 a} = |J_x|$$

The power loss per plate is $\tfrac{1}{2} \bar{J}_x^2 R$, where $R$ is the resistive component of the wave impedance

$$Z = (1 + j) \left[ \frac{\omega\mu_0}{2\sigma} \right]^{\frac{1}{2}}$$

Therefore,

$$R = \left[ \frac{\omega\mu_0}{2\sigma} \right]^{\frac{1}{2}}$$

so that

$$\tfrac{1}{2} \bar{J}_x^2 R = \tfrac{1}{2} \frac{m^2 \pi^2 E_0^2}{\omega^2 \mu_0^2 a^2} \left[ \frac{\omega\mu_0}{2\sigma} \right]^{\frac{1}{2}} \text{ W/m}^2$$

The power transmitted per unit area along the $z$ direction is

$$\frac{\text{power}}{\text{unit area}} = \tfrac{1}{2} \text{ real } (\bar{E} \times \bar{H}^*) \, ds$$

$$\frac{\text{power}}{\text{unit area}} = -\tfrac{1}{2} (\bar{E}_y \bar{H}_x) \, dx \cdot dy$$

where $\bar{H}^*$ is the complex conjugate of $\bar{H}$, and $\bar{E}_y$ and $\bar{H}_x$ are the real parts of the appropriate field components.

Now

$$\bar{E}_y = E_0 \cos(\omega t - \beta z) \sin\left(\frac{m\pi x}{a}\right)$$

$$\bar{H}_x = \frac{-\beta E_0}{\omega\mu_0} \cos(\omega t - \beta z) \sin\left(\frac{m\pi x}{a}\right)$$

$$\frac{\text{power}}{\text{unit area}} = \frac{E_0^2 \beta}{2\omega\mu_0} \sin^2\left(\frac{m\pi x}{a}\right) \, \mathrm{d}x \cdot \mathrm{d}y$$

as $\cos(\omega t - \beta z) = 1$, so that the total power transmitted for 1 m width of waveguide is

$$W = \int_0^a \frac{E_0^2 \beta}{2\omega\mu_0} \sin^2\left(\frac{m\pi x}{a}\right) \mathrm{d}x$$

$$= \frac{E_0^2 \beta a}{4\omega\mu_0} \text{ W/m} \quad (m = 1)$$

so that the attenuation is obtained from

$$\frac{\frac{1}{2}\bar{J}_x^2 R}{W}$$

so

$$\frac{1}{2} \frac{m^2 \pi^2 E_0^2}{\omega^2 \mu_0^2 a^2} \left(\frac{\omega\mu_0}{2\sigma}\right)^{\frac{1}{2}} \frac{4\omega\mu_0}{E_0^2 \beta a}$$

$$\underline{\alpha_{\text{TE}} = \frac{2m^2 \pi^2}{\omega\mu_0 \beta a^3} \left(\frac{\omega\mu_0}{2\sigma}\right)^{\frac{1}{2}} \text{ nepers/m}}$$

## Example 7.9

Derive an expression for the power per unit width transmitted between two parallel conducting planes in the $\text{TE}_{10}$ mode. The distance between the plates is $a$.

## Solution 7.9

This problem will make use of Poynting's vector. For propagation, $\gamma = j\beta$; otherwise, if $\gamma$ is real, only attenuation occurs.

From the basic equations,

$$\bar{E}_y = E_0 \cos(\omega t - \beta z) \sin\left(\frac{\pi x}{a}\right)$$

$$\bar{H}_x = \frac{\beta E_0}{\omega\mu_0} \cos(\omega t - \beta z) \sin\left(\frac{\pi x}{a}\right)$$

Therefore,

$$P = \bar{E}_y \times \bar{H}_x^* = \frac{\beta E_0^2}{\omega\mu_0} \cos^2(\omega t - \beta z) \sin^2\left(\frac{\pi x}{a}\right)$$

Therefore,

$$\int_0^a P \, \mathrm{d}x = \int_0^a \frac{\beta E_0^2}{\omega\mu_0} \cos^2(\omega t - \beta z) \sin^2\left(\frac{\pi x}{a}\right) \mathrm{d}x$$

or

$$P_z = \frac{\beta E_0^2 a}{2\omega\mu_0} \cos^2(\omega t - \beta z)$$

The average value of $P_z$ over one cycle is

$$P_{av} = \frac{\beta E_0^2 a}{4\omega\mu_0} \ \text{W/m}$$

### Example 7.10

Consider a guide consisting of a pair of highly conducting plates. For a plane parallel wave moving in the $z$ direction and having a frequency of 100 MHz, determine the power absorbed per square metre in the plates. Take $\overline{E}_x = 1$ V/m and $\sigma = 5.8 \times 10^7$ S/m.

### Solution 7.10

For this problem, the wave will have the two components, $\overline{E}_x$ and $\overline{H}_y$, together with a component $\overline{E}_z$ (very small) due to the currents in the walls of the guide that are induced by $\overline{H}_y$.

Now, in air,

$$\frac{\overline{E}_x}{\overline{H}_y} = \eta = 120\,\pi\,\Omega$$

so that

$$\overline{H}_y = \frac{1}{120\pi} = 2.65 \ \text{mA/m}$$

For the metal,

$$\eta_m = \left[\frac{\omega\mu_0}{\sigma}\right]^{\frac{1}{2}} \angle 45°$$

$$= \left[\frac{2\pi \times 10^8 \times 4\pi \times 10^{-7}}{5.8 \times 10^7}\right]^{\frac{1}{2}} \angle 45°$$

$$= 3.69 \times 10^{-3} \angle 45° \ \Omega/\text{m}^2$$

Therefore,

$$\overline{E}_z = \eta_m \overline{H}_y = \frac{2.65}{10^3} \times \frac{3.69}{10^3} \angle 45°$$

$$= 9.78 \times 10^{-6} \angle 45°$$

$$\text{Power } P = \frac{1}{\sqrt{2}} \frac{|E_z^2|}{\eta_m} = 18.33 \times 10^{-9} \ \text{W/m}^2$$

Alternative approach:

$$P = \tfrac{1}{2} [\overline{E}_z \overline{H}_y]$$

$$= \frac{|\overline{E}_z||\overline{H}_y|}{\sqrt{2}}$$

$$= \frac{9.78}{10^6} \times \frac{2.65}{10^3} \times \frac{1}{1.414} \ \text{W/m}^2$$

$$= 18.33 \times 10^{-9} \ \text{W/m}^2$$

## Example 7.11

Derive an equation for the propagation of power in a waveguide and for the electric field intensity across the $b$ dimensions of the guide in the $TE_{10}$ mode.

### Solution 7.11

The Poynting vector $= \bar{E} \times \bar{H}^* \; W/m^2$.

(a) For the dominant mode, it is only necessary to consider the fields $\bar{E}_y$ and $\bar{H}_x$ — that is,

$$\bar{P}_z = \bar{E}_y \bar{H}_x$$

but it is also known that

$$\bar{P}_z = \left[\frac{\bar{E}_y}{\bar{H}_x}\right] \bar{H}_x^{\,2}$$

where $\bar{E}_y / \bar{H}_x = \eta$, so that

$$\bar{P}_z = \eta \, \bar{H}_x^{\,2}$$

and

$$\bar{H}_x = H_{max} \sin\left(\frac{\pi x}{a}\right) \sin(\omega t - \beta z)$$

where

$$H_{max} = \frac{E_0}{j \omega \mu_0 \sigma} = \text{peak value of the magnetic field intensity}$$

Then

$$\bar{P}_z = \eta \, H_{max}^{\,2} \sin^2\left(\frac{\pi x}{a}\right) \sin^2(\omega t - \beta z)$$

For one period, the average of the Poynting vector is

$$W_z = \frac{1}{2\pi} \int_0^{2\pi} \eta \, H_{max}^{\,2} \sin^2\left(\frac{\pi x}{a}\right) \sin^2(\omega t - \beta z) \, d(\omega t)$$

$$= \tfrac{1}{2} \, \eta \, H_{max}^{\,2} \sin^2\left(\frac{\pi x}{a}\right)$$

The total power $W_t = \int W_z \; ds$ over the waveguide cross-section.

$$W_t = \tfrac{1}{2} \, \eta \, H_{max}^{\,2} \int_0^a \int_0^b \sin^2 \frac{\pi x}{a} \; dx \cdot dy$$

$$= \tfrac{1}{4} \, \eta \, H_{max}^{\,2} \, ab$$

(b) The peak electric field is found from

$$\bar{E}_y = \eta \, \bar{H}_x = \eta \, H_{max}$$

where

$$H_{max} = 2 \left[\frac{W_t}{\eta a b}\right]^{\frac{1}{2}}$$

174

Thus,

$$\bar{E}_y = 2\left[\frac{\eta W_t}{ab}\right]^{\frac{1}{2}}$$

or

$$W_t = \tfrac{1}{4}\frac{\bar{E}_y^2 ab}{\eta}$$

## Example 7.12

Two sections of rectangular waveguide each have perfectly conducting walls, of inner dimensions $a$ and $0.5a$, enclosing a solid dielectric of relative permittivity 2.25. The two waveguide sections are coupled by a third section of the small wall dimensions, which is air-filled. This waveguide system transmits energy from a source operating at a free-space wavelength of $2.5a$ into a matched load. Explain why the air-filled central section causes the transmitted signal to be attenuated. Determine the value of attenuation of the signal power, in dB, if the air-filled section has a length of $1.5a$.

## Solution 7.12

For the dielectric waveguide

$$\frac{1}{\lambda_g^2} = \frac{2.25}{(2.5a)^2} - \frac{1}{(2a)^2} = \frac{9 - 6.25}{(5a)^2}$$

$$\lambda_g = \frac{5a}{1.658} = 3.015a \text{ (real)}$$

For the air waveguide,

$$\frac{1}{\lambda_g^2} = \frac{1}{(2.5a)^2} - \frac{1}{(2a)^2} = \frac{4 - 6.25}{(5a)^2}$$

$$\lambda_g = \frac{j5a}{1.5} = j\,3.33a \text{ (imaginary)}$$

In the dielectric section, the propagation wave is a normal $\mathrm{TE}_{01}$ mode with $\beta = \dfrac{2\pi}{3.015a}$ rad/m, while, in the air section, the wave is evanescent, with an attenuation factor $\alpha = \dfrac{2\pi}{3.33a}$ nepers/m. Over the length $1.5a$, $e^{-\alpha L} = e^{-2.83} = 0.059$. By similar reasoning $Z_1 = \bar{E}/\bar{H}$ is real for the dielectric and $Z_2 = \bar{E}/\bar{H}$ is imaginary for the air.

There are three factors causing signal attenuation:

(1) Owing to the mismatch between $Z_1$ and $Z_2$, only a fraction of the incident energy crosses the junction to the air-filled section.

(2) Owing to the evanescent mode, there is significant attenuation across the air-filled section.

(3) The mismatch between $Z_2$ and $Z_1$ causes a further loss of energy at the second air–dielectric interface.

Let the incident $\bar{E}$ field at junction A (see diagram) in the dielectric be $|E|$. Then the electric field transmitted through the interface at A is given by

$$|E_t| = |E|\left|\frac{2Z_2}{Z_1 + Z_2}\right| \quad \text{due to the effective match}$$

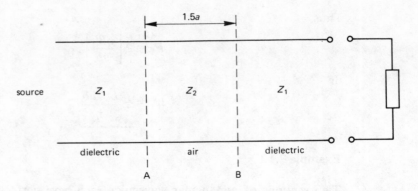

[Reminder: $e^{-2\alpha L}$ is extremely small.] Owing to the evanescent mode, the incident field at junction B in the air section is

$$|E^1| = |E_t| \, e^{-\alpha L}$$

Thus, the field transmitted through the interface at B is

$$|E_t^1| = |E^1| \left| \frac{2Z_1}{Z_1 + Z_2} \right|$$

Thus, the attenuation (power) factor is

$$\frac{|E_t^1|^2}{|E|^2} = \left| \frac{4Z_1 Z_2}{(Z_1 + Z_2)^2} \right|^2 e^{-2\alpha L}$$

Now

$$Z_2/Z_1 = j \, \frac{3.33}{3.015} = j \, 1.1$$

Therefore,

$$\text{attenuation} = \left| \frac{4j1.1}{(1 + j1.1)^2} \right|^2 \times 0.059^2 = \underline{0.014 \text{ nepers/m}}$$

or

$$\underline{0.12 \text{ dB/m}}$$

## 7.3 Unworked Problems

### Problem 7.1

For a waveguide 40 mm by 60 mm, calculate the cut-off frequency in the $TE_{01}$ mode together with the phase velocity and wavelength at a frequency 50 per cent above that of cut-off.

(Leeds Polytechnic)

[2.5 GHz; $4 \times 10^8$ m/s; 107.2 mm]

### Problem 7.2

Derive an expression for the field configurations in the $TM_{10}$ mode of propagation between plane parallel conductors.

$$\left[ \overline{E}_x/\overline{E}_z = \frac{dx}{dy} = - \frac{\beta a}{\pi} \cos(\omega t - \beta z) \cos\left(\frac{\pi x}{a}\right) \right]$$

## Problem 7.3

The cross-section of a rectangular waveguide has dimensions 30 mm by 20 mm. Calculate the cut-off frequency ($f_c$) for the fundamental mode and sketch the field pattern of such a wave within the guide at a frequency of $2f_c$. Explain what will happen should an attempt be made to transmit a wave of frequency less than $f_c$.

For frequencies above the cut-off frequency, sketch the relationship of the wavelength in the guide to free-space wavelength as a function of $f_c/f$, deriving any formulae used. Hence show that the phase velocity of the wave in the guide is greater than the velocity of light, and comment.

(CEI Part 2)

[5 GHz]

## Problem 7.4

(a) Consider a parallel plane waveguide with plate separation of 200 mm with the $TE_{10}$ mode excited at 1 GHz. Find the propagation coefficient $\gamma$, the cut-off frequency $f_c$ and $\lambda_g$, the wavelength, in the guide. Take $\epsilon_r = 1$.

(b) If the space between the conducting plates is now filled with a dielectric material of $\epsilon_r = 4$, find new values for $\gamma$, $f_c$ and $\lambda_g$.

(Leeds Polytechnic)

[(a) $\gamma = j13.85$, 750 MHz, 455 mm; (b) $\gamma = j39.3$, 375 MHz, 160 mm]

## Problem 7.5

Derive an expression for the intrinsic wave impedance of a two-phase waveguide for both the TE and TM modes of operation, in terms of wavelength $\lambda$ and guide wavelength $\lambda_g$.

$$\left[\eta_{TE} = 120\pi \frac{\lambda_g}{\lambda}\left[\frac{\mu_r}{\epsilon_r}\right]^{\frac{1}{2}}; \eta_{TM} = 120\pi \frac{\lambda}{\lambda_g}\left[\frac{\mu_r}{\epsilon_r}\right]^{\frac{1}{2}}\right]$$

## Problem 7.6

Prove by Maxwell's equations that it is impossible for a TEM wave to be propagated inside a conducting tube, whether the guide is cylindrical or rectangular. [Hint: Prove $V$ is constant; therefore, $\overline{E} = 0$ and, hence, $\overline{H} = 0$].

## Problem 7.7

A circular waveguide has a radius $a$. It carries a TE mode of propagation in which the field vectors are independent of the angular coordinate. Derive the fields for the lowest mode of this type and calculate the attenuation of the guide for this mode.

(Leeds Polytechnic)

$$\left[(\omega^2 \mu_0 \epsilon_0 - \beta^2); \alpha = \frac{1}{(2\omega\mu_0\sigma)^{\frac{1}{2}}} \frac{(\omega^2 \mu_0 \epsilon_0 - \beta^2)}{a\beta}\right]$$

## Problem 7.8

The fields of the dominant $TE_{01}$ mode in a rectangular waveguide are of the form

$$\bar{E}_x = E_0 \cos(ky \sin \theta)\, e^{j(\omega t - kz \cos \theta)}$$

$$\bar{H}_y = H_0 \cos \theta \cos(ky \sin \theta)\, e^{j(\omega t - kz \cos \theta)}$$

$$\bar{H}_z = H_0 j \sin \theta \sin(ky \sin \theta)\, e^{j(\omega t - kz \cos \theta)}$$

where $k^2 = \omega^2 \mu_0 \epsilon_0$ and $E_0/H_0 = (\mu_0/\epsilon_0)^{\frac{1}{2}} = \eta$. If the waveguide walls are at $x = \pm a$ and $y = \pm b$, what is the cut-off wavelength in terms of these guide dimensions?

From the above field expressions, describe whether or not the waves would be disturbed by narrow slits cut in the waveguide walls, $y = \pm b$, with the slits parallel to (i) the $x$ axis, (ii) the $z$ axis.

Calculate the total time-average power flow along the guide.

$$\left[\lambda_g = \frac{\lambda}{[1 - (\lambda/\lambda_c)^2]^{\frac{1}{2}}}; \quad \text{(i) slits parallel to } x \text{ axis no effect; (ii) slits parallel to } z \text{ axis considerable effect; } ab\eta \, |H_0|^2 \cos \theta \right]$$

## Problem 7.9

Calculate the average power transmitted and the peak electric field across the $b$ dimension of a waveguide that has a width of 0.07 m and height of 0.035 m. The excitation is carried out in the $TE_{10}$ mode at a frequency of 3 GHz, with a peak magnetic field intensity of 10 A/m at the guide centre. Assume negligible attenuation.

[33 W; 5390 V/m]

## Problem 7.10

A rectangular waveguide is filled with a dielectric material of relative permittivity $\epsilon_r$ except for a section of length $l$, which is empty, as shown in the diagram. The dimensions of the guide have been chosen such that the dominant $TE_{10}$ mode propagates in the dielectric section but is evanescent in the empty section. A wave is incident from the left and a matched load terminates the guide at the right.

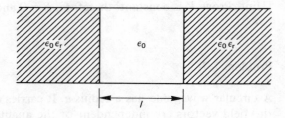

Calculate the power dissipated in the load (in relation to the power in the incident wave) as a function of the length $l$.

$$\left[1 + \left(\frac{\alpha^2 + \beta^2}{2\alpha\beta}\right)^2 \sinh^2 \alpha l, \text{ if } \alpha l \text{ is large, yielding } \left(\frac{\alpha^2 + \beta^2}{4\alpha\beta}\right)^2 e^{2\alpha l}\right]$$

**Problem 7.11**

The fields of the $TE_{10}$ mode in a rectangular waveguide with broad dimension $a$ and narrow dimension $b$ are given by

$$\bar{E}_y = E_1 \sin\left(\frac{\pi x}{a}\right) e^{-j\beta z}$$

$$\bar{H}_x = -\frac{\beta}{\omega\mu} E_1 \sin\left(\frac{\pi x}{a}\right) e^{-j\beta z}$$

$$\bar{H}_z = \frac{j\pi a}{\omega\mu} E_1 \cos\left(\frac{\pi x}{a}\right) e^{-j\beta z}$$

The characteristic impedance of a transmission line can usually be determined from a calculation of: (a) power and longitudinal current or (b) power and transverse voltage or (c) transverse voltage and longitudinal current. Show that for the $TE_{10}$ waveguide, three different answers are obtained, but for TEM transmission lines these three possibilities lead to the same answer. [The transverse voltage can be taken as the line integral of the electric field at the centre of the broad face of the waveguide.]

(Leeds Polytechnic)

$$\left[ (a)\ \frac{\pi^2}{8}\ \frac{k}{\beta}\ \frac{b}{a}\ \eta;\ (b)\ \frac{2k}{\beta}\ \frac{b}{a}\ \eta;\ (c)\ \frac{\pi}{2}\ \frac{k}{\beta}\ \frac{b}{a}\ \eta \right]$$

**Problem 7.12**

A waveguide comprises two extensive and perfectly conducting flat sheets set parallel and distance $a$ apart in air. The propagation mode in the $z$ direction is such that the component field amplitudes in the $y$ direction are

$$\bar{H}_y = 0;\ \bar{E}_y = A \sin\left(\frac{\pi x}{a}\right) e^{-\gamma z}$$

Derive the other components of $\bar{E}$ and $\bar{H}$, and sketch the field patterns in the guide. Derive an expression for the average power transmitted between the sheets in the $z$ direction per unit $y$-axis width.

(CEI Part 2)

$$\left[ \frac{A^2 \beta}{2\omega\mu}\ e^{-2\alpha z} \right]$$

**Problem 7.13**

A matched rectangular air-filled waveguide operating at 15 GHz supports only the $TE_{10}$ mode; 15 GHz is 1.3 times the cut-off frequency of the $TE_{10}$ mode and 0.7 times the cut-off frequency of the next higher order mode. The peak value of the electric field strength in the guide is 1 kV/m. Determine (i) the guide dimensions and (ii) the average power transmitted down the guide.

(Engineering Council)

[0.013 : 0.007 : 0.58 mW]

# Bibliography

It is beyond the scope of a book of this type to provide an extensive list of the many fine published works on field theory. Below are listed a number of books which the author believes will be useful to a student who is making a study of the subject.

Carter, G. W., *The Electromagnetic Field in its Engineering Aspects*. Longman, London

Hayt, W. H. Jr., *Engineering Electromagnetics*. McGraw-Hill, New York

Jordon, E. C. and Balmain, K. E., *Electromagnetic Waves and Radiating Systems*. Prentice-Hall, Englewood Cliffs, N.J.

Kraus, J. D. and Carver, D. R., *Electromagnetics*. McGraw-Hill, New York

Parton, J. E. and Owen, S. J. T., *Applied Electromagnetics*. Macmillan, London

Staniforth, J. A., *Microwave Transmission*. English Universities Press, London

# Index